by
Yair Weinstock

translated by
Miriam Zakon

Published by
Mesorah Publications, ltd

for the
Soul

A famous novelist retells classic stories with passion and spirit

FIRST EDITION
First Impression ... June 1999

Published and Distributed by
MESORAH PUBLICATIONS, LTD.
4401 Second Avenue / Brooklyn, N.Y 11232

Distributed in Europe by
J. LEHMANN HEBREW BOOKSELLERS
20 Cambridge Terrace
Gateshead, Tyne and Wear
England NE8 1RP

Distributed in Israel by
SIFRIATI / A. GITLER
10 Hashomer Street
Bnei Brak 51361

Distributed in Australia and New Zealand by
GOLDS BOOK & GIFT SHOP
36 William Street
Balaclava 3183, Vic., Australia

Distributed in South Africa by
KOLLEL BOOKSHOP
Shop 8A Norwood Hypermarket
Norwood 2196, Johannesburg, South Africa

Typography by CompuScribe at ArtScroll Studios, Ltd.

Printed in the United States of America by Noble Book Press Corp.
Bound by Sefercraft, Quality Bookbinders, Ltd., Brooklyn N.Y. 11232

Table of Contents

Introduction: The Book and the Story

"He lives eternally, on high, His Name is holy;
He created His world with three things:
with a book, with a scribe, with a story."
Sefer Yetzirah (The Book of Creation)

THE STORY HAS AN HONORED PLACE IN THE WORLD OF Judaism. A Jewish child of 5 learns of the early days of history and humanity from among the pages of the *Chumash*. The Torah is inscribed upon his heart and he absorbs it with wonder, because it is told to him as a tale. The world's Creator, the One Who gave us the Torah, in His infinite wisdom, concealed the depths of His Torah in the guise of a story that even a youngster can comprehend. But the tale is nothing more than a cover for the truth, as the holy *Zohar* says *(Bamidbar 153):* "The stories of the Torah are clothing for the Torah."

When the youngster grows a bit older he learns the tales of *Tanach*, in the Books of *Joshua, Judges, Samuel* and *Kings,* in the *Megillahs*, in *Ezra* and *Daniel*. A window to worlds past is opened to him, fashioned with the marvelous power of a holy perspective. The stories offer a pure and clear Jewish vision that builds the child's developing personality layer upon layer, teaching and building him up spiritually.

And when the youngster grows up further and finally begins to study Talmud, he is slowly introduced to the fine, aged wine of *aggadata*, the stories of our Sages. In this miraculous world, in these tales of the Talmud, his soul and spirit are refreshed. From the moment that the student encounters Torah tales, both of the Written and Oral Torah, he is eternally entranced by them.

A person's soul craves stories, desires to travel to faraway places. Grab hold of a story and within seconds you are transported to other worlds, you travel a thousand years into the past, you jump from country to country. You revel in the enchanted world of great men, are astounded by their stature and remarkable deeds. That is the essence and the magic of the tale, enchanting young and old alike.

When I was young I merited being close to the famed *tzaddik*, the *Admor* R' Moshe Mordechai Biderman of Lelov, a man of great holiness and purity. His self-sacrifice, his closeness to G-d, his abstinence, the love of Jews that burned within him, his lofty stature that is almost impossible for us to comprehend — these have become well known to many. In order to properly describe his enormous stature one would need several volumes. It has been said of him that even had he lived among the awesome generation of 150 years ago, he would have been a marvel. Within this short introduction, I wish only to speak of one aspect of his multifaceted personality, and that is his power as a storyteller. When during the *tischen* that he would lead, the rebbe would touch upon a story, he had incredible ability to hold everyone's attention completely. It was from him that I first saw how a story could take a spark of history and bring it to life. Every word was measured and weighed, every story beautifully crafted. There were layers concealed within the words, as he used the genre of the true story to bring healing and salvation: Every word was chosen with its own special intention. It was then that I learned the true value of a story properly told.

At that same time I was learning in the yeshivah of the *gaon* R' Meshulam Dovid HaLevi Soloveitchik, who has taught for many years in Yeshivas Brisk "HaGrach." My rebbe would give a *parashas hashavua shiur* on Shabbos to a select group of students. Occasionally, when the portion of halachah and *aggadata* had been completed, our rebbe would turn to stories, telling us tales that had been heard from his great-grandfather the *Beis HaLevi,* from his grandfather R' Chaim, and from his father, R' Velvel. These tales had the full flavor of times gone by, the magic of better days. They were rooted in the main foundation of Brisk learning, with precision, and an element of accuracy that takes in every detail. Every word in the story was a brick, every tiny detail a tile. Thus tile was placed upon brick, piece by piece, until a wonderful edifice stood before the listener. These stories were clear and alive to us; we could actually see them. We were there when the Rav of Brisk fled the Nazis during the days of destruction; our hearts pounded with terror when a Nazi soldier stopped the carriage that was carrying him and we breathed sighs of relief when he let the Rav go free, as the Rav read the holy words of R' Chaim of Volozhin in his work, *Nefesh HaChaim.*

And thus the foundations were laid for this book.

The majority of these stories are not well known, and some are being printed for the first time. The first to fill my treasure chest was my father, Rabbi Shlomo Menachem Weinstock, one of the notables among Lelov *chassidim,* who grew up among *chassidim* who themselves knew the great men of previous generations. These elderly men generously shared this legacy, as they had known it firsthand, particularly the heritage of the *Admor* R' Dovid Tzvi Shlomo Biderman, the rebbe of Lelov in Jerusalem. From my father I heard many of the stories that appear here, told to me with meticulous attention to detail and accuracy.

I heard many of the stories directly from the elder *chassidim* at *Melaveh Malkahs* and *Rosh Chodesh* dinners in Beis Midrash Beis Dovid of *chassidei* Lelov in Jerusalem. Others come from the notables of Karlin *chassidus*, including the incredible R' Chaim Asher Lederman and R' Zalman Brizel, as well as the *Rosh Yeshivah*, the great R' Yisrael Grossman.

A portion came from my uncle, the kabbalist R' Moshe Yair Weinstock, with whom I merited being close in my younger days. He would tell of things he heard in his youth from the rebbe *HaRadatz*, and from the *chassidim* and great men of the walled city of old Jerusalem, of events that took place more than a century ago.

I heard some stories from my uncle, R' Chaim Eliyahu Sternberg, Rav of Jerusalem's Katamon neighborhood, who was one of the *chassidim* closest to R' Yoel of Satmar. Others I heard from a great scholar and *chassid* who was considered one of Jerusalem's top storytellers, who has asked for anonymity. He himself gathered them from many sources, and his stories are all well documented. These stories bear the stamp of authentic Judaism and the original chassidic movement, passed down from father to son, from teacher to student, preserved like fine wine for coming generations. With all this, I also attempted to check and authenticate all stories. However, no one is perfect, and occasionally differing versions were available.

The stories originally appeared in the periodical *Kol HaShavua*, under the pen name B. Shapira. With Hashem's help the stories gained widespread acceptance and acclaim. Torah teachers and *maggidei shiur* used them in their talks to the public, and *mashgichim* in yeshivahs related them as part of their ethical teachings. But the vast majority were told over the Shabbos table.

At the request of many of my readers, I have now collected some of the stories for this volume, with the hope that these tales of our fathers will stand before their sons, who long to reach the stature of previous generations. This is the first in a series of books that will be published with Hashem's help.

Yair Weinstock
Yerushalayim

Tales for the Soul

Healing Body and Soul

THROUGHOUT HIS YOUTH, R' YEHOSHUA ZANVIL WAS extraordinarily diligent in his Torah study, learning from the generation's greatest scholars. It was no wonder, then, that when R' Yehoshua reached maturity, R' Shmuel Rivkind, one of Vilna's wealthiest men, took him as a husband for his daughter, Sarah Pessil.

After his marriage, the young bridegroom, supported by his father-in-law, studied Torah in tranquility and peace. His wife saw him only once a day; the rest of the time, for 18 straight hours, he closeted himself in a small book-lined room near the attic.

His diligence and fervor were nothing short of astounding. He combined depth of learning with incisive, razor-sharp logic. R' Yehoshua surely seemed destined to blossom into one of the great men of his generation.

R' Shmuel Rivkind's sudden death fell like a terrible blow upon all who knew him. One of Vilna's most upstanding and generous philanthropists had suddenly been taken, in the prime of his life, like a proud oak shattered by lightning. His young son-in-law, particularly, mourned his death, for he knew that without his father-in-law he would never have reached the lofty heights he had climbed.

After the seven days of mourning, his mother-in-law spoke to him. "You know that your late father-in-law respected your Torah learning tremendously, and hoped you would continue studying all your life. And that would have been your future, without a doubt, had he lived. But Heaven has decreed otherwise; he has gone to his rest, leaving us behind. I must see to raising my three orphaned boys by myself."

R' Yehoshua grew faint. It soon became clear to him that his mother-in-law expected him to leave the world of Torah learning and take his deceased father-in-law's place in the business. He objected: He had absolutely no business experience, and commerce was a complete mystery to him. He had lived all his life within the four cubits of Torah study; it was quite likely that he would quickly destroy the entire edifice of wealth that his father-in-law had built so carefully, with such effort, over so many years.

His mother-in-law paid no heed to his arguments. The widow adhered to her position, not budging an inch. "Where there is Torah, there is wisdom," she declared. "With your remarkable talents, you can't help but succeed!"

In a last, desperate effort, he went to speak with his rabbis, hoping they would not permit him to leave the world of Torah. Much to his shock and chagrin, they advised him to listen to his mother-in-law. Bewildered and heartbroken, R' Yehoshua entered his father-in-law's business.

A new world opened before him. He found himself forced to devote his entire day to the family's intricate business dealings. His years of study stood by him during those hours, and the clever suggestions he made to his managers gained much from the sharpness he had acquired from learning. He quickly made himself a name as one of the city's top merchants, resourceful and creative. He increased the family holdings until they grew 10 times as great as they had been during the days of R' Shmuel, just as his mother-in-law had predicted.

As part of his business dealings, R' Yehoshua would often travel far beyond the boundaries of Vilna. First his travels encompassed the entirety of Lithuania and Russia. Later he forged connections with the kingdom of Poland, seeking to build new business ties with some of Poland's largest industrialists. During his journeys, his Gemara was his constant companion, his faithful friend; whenever he had a free moment he learned.

One of his trips took him to the city of Mezeritch. "Who is this man, the *Maggid* of Mezeritch?" R' Yehoshua wondered. R' Yehoshua was far removed from the world of *chassidus,* but he felt no strong opposition to it. In Vilna he had heard opinions both for and against the new movement, but he hadn't taken sides in the controversy. His vast experience, both in learning and in commerce, had taught him not to rush into judgment of a person, and certainly not of an entire movement, without first thoroughly examining the facts.

Wherever he wandered in Mezeritch, he heard astonishing things said in praise of the *Maggid.* Not at all the things he had heard back in Vilna. He felt he could not leave the city until he had thoroughly probed the secret. "I will put before him some of the most difficult questions I've come across in *Shas,* those which I have never solved to my satisfaction. If he can answer them, I will know he is a great man!"

Standing before the *Maggid,* however, R' Yehoshua's bones felt like jelly; his courage completely deserted him. All his carefully planned questions seemed to melt away before this great luminary. In a decided panic, he merely put out his hand in greeting. The holy rabbi shook his hand and stared at him with piercing eyes.

"You should know, my son, that all the medicines that the doctors give the sick have no reality to them. They don't help and they don't harm. Who heals the sick?" All the time he spoke, the *Maggid* held the hand of his confused visitor. "The doctors themselves bring healing with them. Every doctor is accompanied by heavenly angels responsible for health, and it is actually these angels who heal a person. The medicines are just for show. The greater the doctor the greater the angels who accompany him. And the greatest of doctors is accompanied by the angel Rafael himself!"

The *Maggid* then said goodbye, and refused to say another word.

The philanthropist was completely puzzled as he left the *Maggid*. What had the *tzaddik* meant to tell him? Regarding the man's greatness he had not a doubt left. He could see that just by looking at him. But to his great sorrow he did not have a clue as to the significance of the *Maggid's* strange words!

"Am I a doctor, or the son of a doctor?" thought R' Yehoshua to himself. "What difference is it to me who heals the sick, the doctor or his medicine? Perhaps his words are an allegory with some deep meaning hidden within them." But though he repeated the *Maggid's* words over and over he could not make any sense of them. Finally he gave up on the mystery and put the odd encounter out of his mind.

Three months passed. R' Yehoshua forged new business ties with some of Poland's greatest industrialists and returned to Vilna triumphant with economic gain. New horizons had opened before him; it seemed likely that soon he would become one of the generation's richest men.

A man plans, but G-d's will prevails. Almost immediately after his return to Vilna R' Yehoshua grew seriously ill. The top doctors, brought to his bedside, could not cure the dread sickness. In their quest to show that they were doing something, they prescribed medications, made dietary recommendations, and ordered complete bed rest.

The great philanthropist's condition worsened; he grew weaker with every passing day. The people of Vilna did not stint in their efforts: They brought the most renowned physicians in the region and from even further away, all to no avail.

Battling his strange illness were hundreds of Vilna's Jews, scholars and simple men, Talmudic geniuses and those who could merely recite *Tehillim*. All wept bitterly. R' Yehoshua was beloved among his townspeople. He was very generous and many of the city's charitable institutions stood in danger of collapse without his assistance. Rumor had it that he was on his deathbed; everyone waited tensely for the terrible moment. The house was filled with lamenting and wailing.

A royal procession wending its way through Vilna's main boulevard captured the attention of the masses. All eyes turned in amazement toward the elegant carriages pulled by high-spirited horses, the likes of which had never been seen in the city.

"Make way for the Czar of Prussia!" The announcement was heard by everyone, Jew and non-Jew alike, and all shouted enthusiastic hurrahs for His Majesty, who had deigned to grace their city with a royal visit.

Among the Jews some quick thinkers came to an important conclusion. A great ruler always traveled with a great doctor, usually the best doctor in the land. He would usually be a part of the royal entourage, staying close by in case the king suddenly grew ill and had need of him.

The heads of the community, their faces beseeching, called the royal procession to a stop. "Please have mercy and don't be angry," they said to the honor guard, in the face of their fury at the Jews' audacity. Had such a thing ever happened before: to block the Czar's way?

The plea reached the Czar's ears: One of the city's most important Jews was on his deathbed. Could the Czar's personal physician possibly visit him? He would be paid whatever sum he requested.

The Czar of Prussia heeded the plea of the hundreds and hundreds of Jews who surrounded his carriage. His personal physician left the carriage. The crowd was so dense that the man could not reach the ground; the masses lifted him onto their shoulders and carried him to the home of R' Yehoshua.

The royal physician approached R' Yehoshua's bed, his garments sparkling in the light of the twinkling chandeliers that hung from the ceiling. He stared at the dying man, and took his pulse. "Can I revive the dead?" he finally called out angrily. "Why have you called me to this man, who has only a few minutes left to live? Let me out of here!" he said furiously, trying to clear a path to walk through. But the house was filled with hundreds of people; there had not even been room to bring in a chair, and his brief examination had been done standing up. In such a crowd, even with the best of intentions, none could help him to depart.

For 10 minutes the doctor battled the throng blocking his exit, until he was ready to give up. He threw an offhand look at the sick man. To his surprise, there was a clear improvement in the man he had given up for dead.

"One minute!" he called excitedly, approaching the bed. He took R' Yehoshua's pulse: No doubt about it, his heartbeat had strengthened and there was a decided turn for the better.

"Everyone out of the room!" The doctor waved everyone away in a fury. "You're stealing the sick man's air!"

After a thorough examination the doctor handed a prescription to one of the family members. "Quickly, go to the nearest pharmacy. If he takes this medication, he will be healed."

The man left swiftly like a bow from an arrow — and immediately the sick man looked even better.

The doctor was confused. Were he to give the man the strong medication he had just prescribed, it might now, in this new situation, do more damage than good. No, he would have to write up a weaker prescription.

The second messenger left the house no less swiftly than the first but again, before he returned, there was still another change for the better. Color returned to the sick man's cheeks and it was clear that his illness was — incredibly — disappearing, like mist evaporating into the air.

The doctor stood, astounded, wondering how to call back the two messengers and have them bring back still a weaker medication. But he saw the illness leaving the man minute by minute. After a little more time, R' Yehoshua was able to sit up in his bed, just like any healthy person.

When the messengers returned bearing their bottles of medicine, the doctor took them and spilled their contents into the earth. "There's nothing more for me to do here," he said openly. "This man was cured by a clear miracle; I didn't do anything for him."

"The opposite is true." R' Yehoshua spoke for the first time. "Your presence here, together with that of the angel Rafael, who escorts you always, is what cured my illness." He begged the physician to extend his visit for at least a few minutes, until he had completely regained his strength.

R' Yehoshua told the royal physician the story of his visit to the *Maggid* of Mezeritch and the *Maggid's* strange words, which he had not understood until this day.

"Who is this man?" the Czar's doctor asked faintly. "Only a man on whom the Heavenly spirit rests could say such things!"

And something reawakened in the doctor, some teachings of his youth. For the physician, Dr. Aaron Grida, had been a very special soul growing up in the home of his Torah-observant parents. But he had been caught up by the times and had taken on the life of a gentile, until he had almost forgotten his Jewish past. This open miracle moved him deeply. He quickly tendered his resignation to the Czar of Prussia and made his way to Mezeritch.

"I've been waiting for you a long time," the Maggid greeted him, his face beaming. "Let us heal each other. You will heal my body" — for the Maggid suffered from many ailments, particularly in his legs — "and I will heal your soul."

It is said that Dr. Grida never left the *Maggid's* side, not until the *Maggid* had left this world. The doctor's repentance was complete, and he became the famed R' Aharon, counted among the greatest students of the *Maggid* of Mezeritch.

More than an Only Son

THE HEAVY CURTAINS HANGING OVER THE WINDOWS moved gently in the light breeze. The heat wave that had settled upon Cracow at the beginning of the week had begun to break, bringing slightly cooler air in its wake. But beads of sweat still ran down the furrowed brows of the yeshivah students listening with intense concentration to the *shiur* of their teacher, R' Heschel of Cracow.

Hailed as an incredible genius from his earliest youth, R' Heschel was one of the world's great scholars. Even as a youngster, his wise words penetrated the farthest corners of the Jewish Quarter where he lived with his parents. Men enjoyed savoring his insights, repeating them again and again. They derived much pleasure from their sharpness, a wonderful sharpness that reflected a deep understanding of life, a sharpness spiced with wit and humor.

That was his childhood, a taste of greatness to come. For with the passing years, as he grew to young adulthood, Heschel put all his energies into Torah, until he attained remarkable heights. He became known as a master teacher. After he had married and founded a yeshivah, top scholars came to hear his lectures, *shiurim* deep as the sea, with his logic straightforward, sharp, and penetrating.

As much as he was known for his brilliance, so was he famed for his holiness and piety. R' Heschel, like R' Yehudah *HaNasi* in his time, could testify that he had not enjoyed even one finger's worth of this temporal world.

On that summerlike day R' Heschel was lecturing to a select group of his students. But even they could hardly follow the lesson, which was extraordinary in its keen logic. Only two of the pupils followed him, step by step.

Suddenly, the listeners grew alert. R' Heschel had reached the core of the topic and was now unveiling his great *chiddush*. This was a new way to understand what had been said, a startling and bold explanation that undercut all of his previous questions, proving that none of them had any validity.

With great fervor R' Heschel repeated his *chiddush* again and again until all the students understood it, not moving on until the last of the students had mastered his teachings.

And then, pandemonium broke out.

At that time the writings of the great rabbi, Rabbeinu Shmuel Eliezer Idels, known as the *Maharsha,* were making a profound impact on the Torah world. The days when his Torah works were published were days of rejoicing and celebration for the people. The greatest of scholars found extraordinary pleasure, and even the youngest students enjoyed his eye-opening, refreshing *chiddushim.*

The words of the *Maharsha's* Torah echoed through all the study halls, and the yeshivah students savored them eagerly. Each of his insights was repeated tens and hundreds of times, until all could recite them by heart.

What had the holy *Baal Shem Tov* said of him? "Until and including the *Maharsha,* all authors wrote their books with *ruach haKodesh.*"

Now, sitting in the warm *beis midrash* in Cracow, R' Heschel's students, listening to his words, were shocked to realize that their great teacher had uttered a *chiddush* that directly contradicted the words of the *Maharsha* on the same topic. Even more, he had taken his colleague's insights and ground them down, pulverizing them into dust.

"Rabbi," one of the students stood up and said courteously, "this *chiddush* is the opposite of that which the *Maharsha* wrote."

R' Heschel had always been prepared to humble himself before the *Maharsha,* that great pillar of Torah recognized by all of world Jewry. But scholars, in their fervor to find the truth, pay no attention to anything not pertinent to the topic. Burning with the fire of Torah, totally engrossed in his lecture, R' Heschel paid less attention than usual to his reply. His response was not, Heaven forbid, insulting, but perhaps was not quite appropriate to the honor of the *Maharsha*.

Had they not been two giants of the earth, the *Maharsha* on one side, R' Heschel on the other, perhaps the troubles would not have come upon him. But this was the *Maharsha* and R' Heschel — and we know that G-d judges such men with intense rigor. A voice in the Yeshivah on High made the pronouncement: Because R' Heschel had not, in view of his greatness, been careful enough with the honor of the *Maharsha,* it was decreed that R' Heschel would not merit to ever publish his own insights on Torah!

R' Heschel, who was one of the privileged few of this world, heard the announcement. His heart thumped wildly in fear and anguish. He immediately left the lectern. None of his students knew why.

R' Heschel had one essay that he had secreted away with his treasures, his *chiddushim* on *Maseches Bava Kamma.* This essay was more beloved to him than an only son to his father. He had devoted many years of concentrated effort into the essay, putting into it the best of his insights culled from his lectures, plus his own private *chiddushim.* R' Heschel had, once or twice, shown selected pages to his friends, who had trembled in disbelief. "This essay will cast new light on the entire *Bava Kamma,*" they told him. Everyone waited anxiously for the day the essay would find its place on the printing press.

Time and time again R' Heschel wondered: Did that heavenly pronouncement include his essay on *Bava Kamma?* Finally he came to the conclusion that it did not.

"This essay," R' Heschel argued to himself, "could have been published already. But what happened? I didn't have the time to deal with it, nor the cash for the publishing expenses. It seems, then, that the work would already be considered public property. That declaration in the Heavenly Yeshivah was a decree only on those new *chiddushim* that I worked out from that day on."

R' Heschel saved, penny by penny, until he had a large enough sum for the printing costs. He chose the best and most responsible of his students. "I have chosen you for this most important task," he whispered into the ears of the excited young man. "You shall travel to Livorno, Italy, to supervise the entire printing process." In those days, there were no printing presses in Poland, thus necessitating the journey.

As he placed the pages into his student's hands, he repeatedly warned him, "This is my entire life. If they are lost, what is life to me? Guard them as you would your own life!"

The student departed on his journey, the precious writings in his trunk. He hardly tasted food or closed his eyes, he was so anxious about the work. Again and again he raced to check on the papers, to make certain they were not lost or tampered with; his rabbi's words had placed great responsibility upon him.

Most of the journey was uneventful. He reached Italy, and only one river lay between him and the city of Livorno. He only had to cross the river and tomorrow he would rush to the printer.

As he reached the middle of the river, a stormy wind suddenly blew, tossing the small ship back and forth. The ship was not a sturdy one; its shaky beams began to blow apart in the gale's fury. Soon it had disappeared, like a stone, in the dark waters.

Only a few travelers survived the doomed ship, among them R' Heschel's student, who latched onto a girder that floated by on the roaring waves and held onto it for his life.

The young man made it to the shore with only the clothing on his back. After he had thanked his Creator for having saved him from certain death, he realized that, in truth, he would have been far better off had he drowned.

"If they are lost, what is life to me?" The words of his rabbi thundered in his ears, entering his heart like the stab of a dagger.

"His worst fears have been realized!!" he moaned bitterly. "How the rabbi trembled for his writings. Oh! Lost! How can I return to Poland? I won't be able to lift my eyes and gaze at my rabbi's face. And how will the rabbi react? He may collapse dead, Heaven forbid, from sorrow, when he hears the mournful news! Or he may look straight at me — and fire will come from his eyes —"

Necessity is the mother of invention, as the proverb says. In his despair, the student came up with an idea brilliant in its simplicity.

He would not return to Poland at all. He would write to his colleagues there, tell them what had happened — and they would know what to do.

When the students in Poland read the letter, their hearts grew faint. Their rabbi's love for his writings on *Bava Kamma* was well known; the scholar would constantly peer into the pages, review them repeatedly. How were they to tell their esteemed teacher the terrible news?

They sat together exchanging ideas, one saying this and the other suggesting that. It was clear that a solution would never be found that would satisfy all.

"I'll tell the rabbi," one finally said, standing.

"Be careful. You're risking your soul," his friends implored him. "You might destroy two: yourself and the rabbi."

But this student was blessed with Solomonlike wisdom. He gave them a meaningful glance and said, "Doesn't anyone have confidence in me? Just wait and see what happens."

In a lesson not long afterwards, the canny student managed, in a roundabout way, to have R' Heschel quote the mishnah (*Berachos* 54a), "A man is obligated to bless for the bad just as he blesses for the good." Rava explains (ibid. 60b), "To accept {misfortunes} with joy."

"Rabbi, I don't understand," the student said. "How can it be? To make a blessing on evil tidings with the same joy that you bless good news?"

"Absolutely," R' Heschel thundered. "Only in man's eyes is there a difference between good news and bad; nothing bad can come from G-d. Whatever He gives us, we have to accept with the exact same feeling! We must realize that what we perceive as bad is really good; the two are alike!"

"But Rabbi," the student's voice grew louder, "if G-d brings something bad upon me — it's bitter, so bitter. How can I bless Him and joyously thank Him during such a terrible time?"

R' Heschel grew fiery, speaking in a voice that could have pierced solid rock. He repeated one of his well-known and beloved lectures, explaining to all the students, and particularly to this insistent young man, how much a person must recognize his own worthlessness. Far better for him not to have been born. G-d owes him nothing and he must accept with humility all that He gives him.

At that moment R' Heschel soared to great heights of spiritual attainment, cleaving almost perfectly to his Creator.

The students exchanged glances. This, then, was their chance!

The student approached R' Heschel and in a whisper related the contents of the letter received from Livorno.

R' Heschel's face grew pale as death. He collapsed onto the floor, unconscious.

His students labored long and hard to bring their teacher back to life, wetting his face with cold water and rubbing his forehead. Finally, he regained consciousness. He looked at them dully: It seemed that the burning light of his eyes had been extinguished, and his soul was ready to part from the prison of its body.

The days passed. R' Heschel returned to normal and resumed giving his lectures. "Tell us, Rabbi," his students asked him, "on the day that the rabbi reaches such lofty heights, explaining how one must accept bad tidings with joy, on that very same day he faints when he hears bad news? How could it be?"

R' Heschel answered somberly. "You should know, my beloved students, that it was your wisdom and cleverness that kept me alive. The lost essay was so beloved to me that I truly meant what I told your colleague before he left: Life was nothing without it. If you hadn't forced me to climb high, high up to the level of accepting His will with joy — I would have died at that very moment. But you provided the medicine before the blow struck, and so my life was saved. Because, you know, a man must rejoice in all that happens to him!"

If a Man Digs a Pit —

DUST MOTES FILLED THE AIR, DANCING IN EVERY CORNER, covering everything. The entire panorama, from one end of the horizon to the next, was yellow. Endlessly yellow. Wherever one turned, he could not see more than that saffron-colored dust settling on every dune and mound. One who cast his eyes upwards, away from the dreary ocherous dust and towards the blue sky, immediately turned away; it was impossible to stare at the glare of the sun.

A caravan of three horses and riders crossed the desert. The horses lifted their hoofs with difficulty, their tongues lolling from thirst. A few days' journey had squeezed them dry.

One of the riders shaded his eyes with his hand and squinted into the distance. "No sign of any life on the horizon," he said in disappointment.

"Don't give up, Ezra," his friend replied. "By my calculations we're just half a day's ride from Baghdad."

"What are you saying, Yechezkel?" the third spoke up. "We can't take the chance of desecrating Shabbos. Don't forget, today is Friday!"

"Did I say we'd have to ride on Shabbos? Masoud, do you suspect me of that?" Yechezkel said resentfully. "We'll ride until noon. If we see Baghdad ahead of us, good. If we don't see it — we'll turn Shabbos into sand."

"There you go!" Masoud fumed. "You're planning to desecrate the Shabbos!"

"Heaven forbid!" Yechezkel answered.

"But didn't you just say you'll turn Shabbos into sand?"

"Yes, we'll turn it into sand — by keeping Shabbos here in the desert sand." Yechezkel chortled happily, enjoying the way his innocent friend had fallen into his punster's trap.

And they did, indeed, turn Shabbos into sand. They traveled until noon without seeing a glimpse of civilization. They reined in their horses, hammered pegs into the ground, and soon a comfortable tent waved in the breeze.

Experienced men, these, and well versed in the ways of the desert. This was not the first time they had spent Shabbos in a barren and dark place. From their experience they knew that this bare desert, that was so quiet and still during the night, was actually alive with bands of robbers who roamed under cover of darkness stealing from unwary travelers. They therefore dug a deep pit and hid their money within, following the wisdom of Shmuel (*Bava Metzia* 42): "Money has no protection other than the earth."

After the Shabbos meal and the singing they all lay down. Within a short time they were fast asleep.

But not all of them.

One of the partners had waited for this moment. From the time they had secreted their money in the earth, a spark of greed had awakened within him. Once he had made certain that his partners were both fast asleep the spark grew into a flame.

"They'll never be able to find out who did it," he murmured to himself. Feverishly he dug in the sand until he found the money. He then cached it in another hole that he dug nearby. His friends slept all the while, the contented sleep of Shabbos.

"Excellent," the thief chuckled in satisfaction. "A nice amount of money is waiting for me, last month's entire profit. Next week I'll come back and retrieve it."

The partners awoke Sunday morning and prepared to continue their journey to Baghdad. But when they dug into the earth they were horrified to find that not one coin remained within the shifting sands.

"One of us is a thief!" the three cried out in unison. Each began to berate and accuse the other two, almost coming to blows.

"My friends, stop this!" Yechezkel cried. "Are we going to kill each other over a few coins? There is justice and there is a judge!"

"But how can the judges decide among us?" Ezra wailed. "Judges know their law, but their job isn't to know every secret. How will they tell us which of the three has taken the money?"

"I didn't say we'd go to a court," Yechezkel explained. "We'll go to the home of the new rabbi of Baghdad, the *gaon* R' Yosef Chaim.

They say that the spirit of G-d rests upon him. I've heard tell that in his vast wisdom he has rooted out deep secrets and uncovered many mysteries."

There were only a few hours between them and Baghdad, and yet those hours dragged along endlessly because of the dark and heavy atmosphere that lay upon them. After the discovery of the theft and the subsequent fight, a curtain of hostility and suspicion fell over them. Two of them suspected the other two, and even the thief put on a show of anger, like an experienced actor.

The imposing turrets of ancient Baghdad loomed in front of them, as if in welcome. Palm trees encircled the city, offering weary travelers a bit of shade. The waters of the Chidekel flowed serenely beneath them as they passed over the bridge that spanned the river. They rode directly to the home of the rabbi.

R' Yosef Chaim heard the story from each of the partners. Indeed, this was an unsolvable mystery. Here were three men, each bursting with accusations, each claiming that one of the other two was a thief, while he was absolutely innocent.

"I am prepared to give my verdict," he finally said, "but first, let me tell you a story."

One warm day, at twilight, the young princess, the king's 12-year-old daughter, went out to enjoy the fresh air. She lingered for quite a while among the orchards, drinking the clear cool air deep into her lungs. This unsupervised walk seemed to cast a spell upon her, for she had never before wandered more than a few footsteps away from the palace, unless accompanied and observed by the careful eyes of her chaperones and guards.

Night fell, and a deep darkness shrouded the countryside. The king's daughter realized that she had lost her way; suddenly, she found herself on a desolate road. She burst out crying, her heart full of foreboding.

She was still weeping bitterly when a wandering pauper passed by and asked her why she was crying. She told him of her plight. "You need the king's palace?" he answered. "That's no problem. I am familiar with all the roads; I'll take you there."

"How do you know all the roads?" the lost girl asked.

"I buy eggs from the villages and travel among the towns selling my wares," the pauper replied.

The wanderer immediately proceeded to display his proficiency. The dark roads that had seemed so threatening turned into friendly paths. In a short time the lost girl stood in her father's palace, unharmed and relieved.

The princess, deeply touched, had no idea how to thank her benefactor, who had taken her from the darkness into the light. Suddenly, she swore that when the time came she would marry no one but him.

The egg seller laughed when he heard her fervent declaration. "Silly princess, I just wanted to save you from the scoundrels who pass along the road. Why make such a fuss about thanking me?"

"No, no!" the princess said heatedly. "I will not marry anyone but you!"

"Very nice," the man laughed. "A princess married to a penniless old beggar. Very, very nice."

The years passed. The princess, who'd been a young girl when she had lost her way, grew up. Kings and rulers began knocking at the castle door, bringing enchanting proposals of marriage. The princess refused to listen: She remained faithful to the egg merchant and refused all offers. But one day the son of one of the most powerful kings in the area was suggested as her spouse, and her father forced her to accept the young heir.

After the royal wedding, that had electrified the entire nation, the young couple exited gracefully. But beneath her veil, the princess broke out in bitter tears.

"What's the matter?" the prince asked, shocked.

"I am a sinner," the bride moaned. "Tonight I have broken my vow!" Between sobs she told her husband of the promise she had made to the impoverished egg seller.

The prince, who was a very wise man, realized that nothing he could say would pacify her. "You're absolutely right," he said simply. "We must go find that wandering man and hear from his own lips whether he holds you to your childhood promise or is willing to forgo it."

The young couple rode many long hours in their beautifully decorated coach until they found the man's hut on the outskirts of the city. They knocked loudly upon his door, waking him from his sleep.

"The princess has come to me?" The pauper stood before them, shocked. "The royal couple couldn't find a more fitting place to spend their wedding night than a poor wanderer's hovel?"

The princess then explained their mission. When he heard the princess's words, tears dropped from the pauper's eyes. The princess's nobility touched his heart. He immediately stood up and declared: "I completely absolve the vow of that 12-year-old girl. I have no complaints to make to you, and no demands."

A heavy stone rolled off the princess's heart; the last obstacle to happiness was gone. Now there was nothing to mar her wedded joy.

The coach's wheels had just begun to roll away and suddenly, as if from underground, a new obstacle appeared: an obstacle in the guise of a band of armed robbers that had followed the royal couple for several hours, waiting for the chance to steal the expensive wedding gifts in their possession.

The drawn swords and flash of murder in the bandits' eyes showed the young couple that these rogues would not be content with mere robbery. The bride and groom fell upon their knees and begged for their lives. In tears, the princess told the leader of the gang why they had come to this deserted place, of the vow she had sworn, and how she had kept her faith with the old pauper who had protected her so long ago.

The cruel heart of the gang leader softened; the princess's tale awoke some long-lost emotion within him. He freed the bride and groom and let them go, without taking even one gold coin!

"You know," R' Yosef Chaim turned to the three merchants, "I have always wondered: Who is the hero of the story? Was it the princess, who kept the promise that she had made to the miserable beggar who had given her a few moment's help? Or the pauper, perhaps, who could have grabbed the chance to go from being nothing to being the husband of the king's wealthy daughter?

"Or perhaps," R' Yosef Chaim gave the three a piercing glance, "it was the gang leader who had done the greatest thing? He could have asked for a huge ransom; the king would surely have given a treasure to redeem his daughter and her new husband; nothing would have been too great. With the wave of a hand the robber gave it all up, not even taking their money!

"Now that three wise merchants, among the most respected in Baghdad, have come to me, I thought to myself, now is the time to clarify this question. What do you think of the story?"

The merchants sat deep in thought. R' Yosef Chaim had drawn a clear picture, one that had left them almost hypnotized. The tale echoed in the room, and in their imagination they could clearly see robbers and princes, dark forests and splendid coaches...

And here was the voice of Masoud, speaking.

"The princess is clearly not the hero; she was just a foolish girl, there was nothing in what she did. The pauper was wise. He knew his place, and realized that an unfortunate egg merchant had no business being a king's son-in-law.

"But," Masoud continued, "the chief of the robbers is clearly a valorous man. The couple was completely in his power. Even if he didn't kill them, he could have taken their money, and yet he didn't touch it!"

"Confess, culprit!" R' Yosef Chaim's eyes flashed. "You are the thief. You stole your partners' money. Your thoughts are preoccupied with nothing but wealth!"

The merchant's voice trembled. "Our rabbi is a man of G-d. You have seen it in prophecy, how I took all the money out of one pit and hid it in a pit that I had dug."

"I saw nothing in prophecy," the rabbi answered. "You dug the pit yourself — with your own words!"

Hillel the Tzaddik and Hillel the Wicked

"*ECHAH DODI LIKRAS KALLAH...*" THE *BAAL TEFILLAH* soared into the ancient melody, an enchanting tune familiar to all those praying together. Everyone joined in the *chazzan's* fervent prayer, sung with all the flourishes. The cantor used his vocal cords like a violinist moves his bow across the strings to produce the richest and most wondrous sounds. His glorious singing opened the locked hearts of all who heard him; this was a song that reached the souls of all Jews.

And when the *chazzan* sang the words, "city of royalty, come out," the men could almost feel the flapping of wings in the heavens, as the celestial city of Jerusalem flew down from its appointed place in the cosmos to listen to the consoling, encouraging words rising up from the old synagogue in the small eastern European village, a village whose only claim to fame was that it permitted Jews to live within its borders.

On that Shabbos eve the *chazzan* surpassed himself, leading the congregation to lofty heights previously unknown.

After the service, groups of congregants stood outside, speaking of the Shabbos pleasure they had derived from the *chazzan*, R' Pinya Zisser.

"Oh, Pinya, Pinya," the mayor of the Jewish community patted him gently on his shoulder, "your name suits you: Zisser, sweet. The beauty of your voice certainly sweetens our lives!"

The mayor set the tone for the rest; everyone followed him to gratefully shake the *chazzan's* hand. "Good for you, Pinya. May G-d continue to grant you favor, and may your prayers be accepted with good will."

"The angels themselves took the trouble to come and hear your song," one of the congregants said in wonder — one of those, obviously, who enjoyed a bit of exaggeration.

When they had all finished expressing their feelings of pleasure, the *shul* began to empty. But a new group now began to congregate, smaller in number and quieter than the previous one. These men stood next to a large wooden beam, near the lectern belonging to Reb Nachum Tzvi, the community activist appointed that month to take care of the poor.

Quiet and embarrassed the men gathered there, impoverished visitors who chanced to be in that town for Shabbos. In meek voices they asked Reb Nachum Tzvi to show them which philanthropic Jews would welcome them to their meal.

The community activist did his work well and faithfully. "You will eat with Zelig the blacksmith," he told one. "And you," he instructed one bashful beggar whose eyes bespoke a certain nobility, "you will be the guest of the Rav."

Reb Nachum Tzvi noticed one of the men who sat quietly learning a complex portion of Gemara. "Ah ha!" he cried out happily. "You are clearly an outstanding scholar. You will go to the mayor of the community."

Another guest, another two guests; no man remained within the *beis midrash* without a place to go for the Shabbos meal.

No man remained; the figure that stood hidden behind the furnace, pouring his heart out to his Creator, completely one with the holiness of Shabbos, could not be called a man. He was almost an angel.

This was R' Zusia of Hanipole, still in his youth, in the years of his exile, wandering from village to village, from town to town. Now he stood, hidden behind the wide brick oven, completely engulfed in his prayers, whispering his secrets to the One Who had formed him.

At first he had listened to the beautiful singing and his heart had danced together with the congregation, though he himself, following the dictates of modesty, had not left his place to join the circle.

No one saw him; no one felt his presence.

The hour was late when R' Zusia finished his prayers. He raised his eyes and saw that he was alone in the *beis midrash*. The oil candles had mostly burned out; the few that still gave off a bit of light cast giant, strange shadows on the sooty walls.

R' Zusia left the *beis midrash* and, without anyone showing him the way, went directly to the home of Reb Nachum Tzvi.

Reb Nachum Tzvi stood at his door, shocked at the sight of the man who had not found a host. "I was sure that everyone was settled. How did I miss you?" His voice could not conceal his wonder.

R' Zusia ignored the question and repeated his own. "Where may I eat this Shabbos?"

"If you had asked me that question two hours ago, it would have had an easy solution," the community worker answered, mildly resentful. "But when I was giving out places to all our guests you hid yourself somewhere. Now what can I do, my son? What family can I send you to, when everyone has finished eating?"

"And so am I to remain hungry and without a Shabbos meal?"

The man rubbed his forehead in dismay. Suddenly, his eyes lit up.

"Are you a scholar, perhaps?"

"If so?"

"Then you can eat at the table of the mayor of our community," Reb Nachum Tzvi exclaimed excitedly. "The mayor is a great scholar, one who has all of Gemara in the palm of his hand. He loves to spend his meal sharing *chiddushei Torah*, and every Shabbos dozens of noted scholars join his table. In his house the meal is of secondary importance, and the learning is paramount. If you are a learned man you can join his meal, for it lasts until the wee hours of the morning."

"Very nice," R' Zusia answered, "but I don't know how to learn."

Reb Nachum Tzvi was confused. Here stood before him a man of obvious stature, saying such things so casually.

"Impossible," he waved away the words. "You obviously are following the words of our Sages, who instructed us (*Bava Metzia* 23b) that the wise may deviate (from the truth) in their speech about three things — and one of them is how much he has learned."

"Heaven forbid," the guest objected strenuously, "I'm not lying. I have said the absolute truth. I don't know how to learn, absolutely not!"

The man grew more perplexed. He studied all aspects of the problem. On the one hand, he remembered the mayor's firm orders not to send any ignorant Jews to his table, only scholars and learned men. On the other hand —

"I've got it!" he finally exclaimed happily, "I'll take you to the mayor's home and sneak you in among the others, without his ever noticing."

And before the guest could say a word, Reb Nachum Tzvi grabbed his hand and hastily walked with him toward the mayor's home.

The sounds of debate and shouting greeted them as they entered the luxurious home of the community's leader. Dozens of guests sat around an extraordinarily large table. Crumbs of challah and a few lone fish bones lay unnoticed upon the snow-white tablecloth. All attention was directed at the current topic — understanding the simple meaning of a complex *Tosafos*. One of the assemblage erupted with a brilliant explanation, reawakening the furor which had just begun to die down.

In the meantime, Reb Nachum Tzvi seated R' Zusia at the table, between two men waving thumbs at each other in the heat of battle. Reb Nachum Tzvi immediately snuck away, and ran for his life...

At first no one noticed the presence of a new visitor, but when R' Zusia made *Kiddush* on the wine, he seemed to leave this world completely, and his loud voice drew everyone's glance. The visitor drank up his wine, and his host then turned to him.

"Young man, who brought you here?"

"Reb Nachum Tzvi," the guest answered quietly.

"So, you must know something of *Shas* and can join our discussion."

"No," the guest corrected him. "I don't know how to learn."

A cloud darkened the mayor's brow. "You have undoubtedly heard that only scholars eat at my table."

"And I don't know how to learn," R' Zusia repeated.

"*Nu?*"

R' Zusia lowered his eyes and sat, silent.

The host searched for a way out. He had always been very careful to follow the dictates of R' Yehudah *HaNasi*, who said (*Bava Basra* 8a): "Woe is me, that I have given of my bread to an unlearned person…"

"Impossible that a Jew does not know even one chapter, one *mishnah.*"

"No, no," the guest answered tranquilly, "I know nothing."

The mayor's eyes darkened. "So why have you come to me? Get out of my house!"

The hostess, the mayor's wife, could not remain quiet in the face of the others' silence. She cried out, pleading, "How can you throw someone out of your home? You don't want him to join you and the others at the meal, fine; but don't throw him out in shame."

The host thought about it and agreed: He gave the guest two small challahs and showed him to a small table in a corner of the hallway. There R' Zusia sat, alone.

When the company grew intoxicated — intoxicated with the words of Torah, that is — they remembered the guest eating in solitude, singing Shabbos songs to himself. The more observant among them saw that the man had left physical pursuits behind and his quiet song was piercing the heavens in its sanctity.

After *bentching*, the men stood up and surrounded R' Zusia's small table.

"We've discussed it and decided that it is humility that causes you to claim you can't learn. We so want to hear some wisdom from you."

"I've already said it, I'm a complete ignoramus, an empty pit that contains nothing," R' Zusia stood his ground.

"How can it be?" the mayor himself interjected. "Were you raised by non-Jewish shepherds? Have you never heard a piece of Torah said? Even one verse?"

The guest thought for a moment. "Yes," he finally said, "one piece of Torah I can tell you —"

With a shout of triumph the men approached his table, broad smiles lighting up their faces. Who knew what secrets of Torah would now be revealed?

"So open your mouth and teach us!" the mayor ordered.

"It's a contradiction that I once noticed," R' Zusia began.

"It must be incredible," one of the guests said.

"A contradiction as tough as iron," another added.

"Quiet," a third shouted. "Let's hear."

"There is an absolute contradiction," the guest continued, unfazed, "between something quoted in the Haggadah and a verse of *Tehillim*."

"Oh, my!" Muffled laughter could be heard. "Have you heard? A contradiction between the Haggadah and *Tehillim*."

"In the Pesach Haggadah, it states, 'In memory of the Temple, as Hillel did.' It seems from this that Hillel was a *tzaddik*," R' Zusia continued in a confident voice. "For if Hillel had not been a pious man, would all of Israel have followed his custom? Yet it states (*Tehillim* 10:3), 'For the wicked man glories (*hillel*, in Hebrew) in his heart's desires.'"

A great roar of laughter exploded in all corners of the hallway. The guests and their host held their stomachs, doubled over in laughter. Such nonsense, such "Purim Torah," they hadn't heard in a long while.

"And what is the answer to the contradiction?" they finally asked, their eyes still moist with tears of laughter. "Have you figured out how to answer the problem?"

R' Zusia turned a face to them as serious as during the last moments of the Yom Kippur service. Giving the mayor a glance that could pierce through him he said, "Yes, there is an answer. Hillel of the Haggadah is truly pious. And the proof is that at the beginning of the evening, just as one returns from the synagogue, he stands next to the door and announces loudly, 'All who are poor shall come and eat, all who are needy shall come and make Pesach.' He doesn't check to see if the poor man is also a scholar.

"Conversely, we look at 'Hillel' of *Tehillim*." R' Zusia turned a scorching eye toward his host. "This Hillel is a completely wicked man. And why? The verse says the wicked man shall boast *(hillel)* of his heart's desire. The evil Hillel sacrifices everything for his passions, worships his desires, and does whatever he wants: The world belongs only to him!"

A deadly silence fell upon the group. Taunting smiles disappeared, replaced by terrified countenances. This man was no ignoramus, far from it. Now everyone understood that the "ridiculous" words had meaning, though only one truly understood how deep they went.

When the guests had left, the mayor quietly followed R' Zusia on his return journey to the darkened *shul*. When the two were alone, the mayor fell to the floor before R' Zusia and burst into bitter tears.

"I'm dirt at your feet, holy man," he sobbed. "Forgive me for having humiliated you."

"You are forgiven, you are forgiven," R' Zusia said gently. But the mayor, deeply moved, was not satisfied. He continued to weep, his body trembling.

"How did you know that my name is Hillel? This is the first time you've ever laid eyes on me. Not one of the other guests knew my first name; all call me 'Mayor.' How did you hit the target so perfectly?"

R' Zusia placed the mayor's hands in his and began lamenting bitterly, "Woe to you, Zusia, that you have done this particular sin on this particular day. Woe to your soul, Zusia, for in this place you did a terrible sin." And R' Zusia enumerated all of "his" sins to the mayor — but the mayor recognized the sins as his own personal property.

R' Zusia listed for Hillel, the mayor, the many sins and crimes that Hillel had committed from the moment he became bar mitzvah up to that very day; nothing was omitted. Slowly he built up the terrible picture of a violent and sinful man who had forcibly grabbed the post of mayor and yet hid behind the mask of a scholar so great he would not share a piece of bread with an ignoramus.

The more R' Zusia added to the list of "his" sins, which were nothing more than a faithful reflection of those of the mayor, the louder Hillel's sobs grew. "Show me the way to repentance," the mayor shouted from the depths of his heart.

"That I cannot do," R' Zusia said. "It is beyond me. But my rabbi and teacher, who is the holy *Maggid* of Mezeritch, can purify your soul, cleanse it of all stain. He will certainly change 'Hillel the wicked' into 'Hillel the *tzaddik*'."

Welcome

R' BARUCH OF MEZIBUZH WAS 4 YEARS OLD WHEN HIS HOLY grandfather, R' Yisrael *Baal Shem Tov*, known as the *Besht*, died, on Shavuos of 5520 (1760). Little Baruch was particularly beloved by his grandfather, who often played with him. He would hold him on his lap and ask, "My Baruch'l, what are you learning?"

The little one would point to the Gemara lying on the table and say, "I'm learning *Bava Kamma*."

"And what does '*Bava Kamma*' mean?" the *Besht* would prompt.

"ברוך בן אדל קדש מבטן אמו" — "Baruch ben Udel, holy from his mother's womb," the young prodigy would answer, spelling out his name in the Gemara's initials. How the grandfather would marvel at the youngster's clever answer.

When the soul of the *Baal Shem Tov* flew heavenward, his students accepted the authority of "The Great *Maggid*," R' Dov Ber of Mezeritch. Later, when his disciple, R' Pinchas of Koritz, became a leader as well, R' Baruch studied with him, and with R' Yaakov Yosef HaKohen of Polonya, the *Baal HaToldos*.

R' Baruch was completely immersed in the service of his Creator. He hardly noticed the world around him. Like Choni

HaMe'ageil in his time, he drew a circle around himself and never stepped out of its limits.

When R' Baruch was 20 years old, important and pious men began to implore him to take on the mantle of leadership. R' Baruch refused. "I don't deserve such a position; I cannot sit on the throne of my grandfather."

Time after time R' Baruch refused the requests. He honestly believed he did not deserve the crown of authority. Thus he locked himself into the four cubits of Torah learning and prayer, going only from home to *beis midrash*, from *beis midrash* to home.

An entire year passed in this manner, R' Baruch remaining adamant in his refusal of a leadership role. But his followers did not despair. They came up with a brilliant scheme. If you can't catch a fish with a line, try a net.

One day, R' Baruch found a carriage waiting near his house. A few men who had routinely sought audiences with him called to him to join them outside. Without a word, R' Baruch went out and stepped into the carriage.

"Holy Rabbi," one of the men said exultantly, once the horses began to move at a gentle gallop, "we're traveling to the city of Tulchin. A large number of Jews await you there, Jews who are thirsting to hear your words of Torah. There you will begin to don the mantle of leadership."

R' Baruch was very clever. He realized immediately what they had planned: That innocent invitation to join them for a bit of fresh air, as they had told him in the beginning, was nothing more than a tactic to get him out of his house and crown him rebbe of Tulchin. But it would not happen, he resolved — no one would crown him against his will, with a crown that would not fit him properly.

"Your efforts are for naught," he told his followers.

"Why?" The men grew suddenly afraid.

"I'm not going with you," he answered serenely. "You can do whatever you want to me: I will not be a rebbe."

"Hundreds of Jews are impatiently awaiting you in Tulchin," one of his "kidnappers" beseeched him. "And if these thirsty people want so much to drink your blessed waters, what sin have they done?"

R' Baruch curled himself into his overcoat and didn't answer.

The celebration had come to an end. The men had been sure that if they forced R' Baruch, he would accept the "judgment" without putting obstacles in their path. They hadn't expected such opposition. The bottles of wine they had prepared in straw-lined baskets lay sealed, with no one expressing interest in them. Huge hampers of cookies and all sorts of goodies remained untouched. The carriage made its sad way toward Tulchin; the travelers' spirits seemed to have fallen onto the ground beneath it.

"I thought we were traveling to a party, but it seems it's Tishah b'Av today," the driver of the coach muttered. No one bothered answering him; everyone was sunk in melancholy.

After sunset and the *Minchah* and *Maariv* prayers, the travelers turned their eyes to the road. It seemed strange to them, unrecognizable.

"Which way are you taking?" they asked the driver. He wrinkled his forehead, rubbed his chin in perplexity, and said, "I don't know what happened. We've made a mistake somewhere."

"An experienced driver like you suddenly doesn't know his way to Tulchin?" the travelers lashed out at him. "How could you have become lost without knowing it?"

The unfortunate driver now had another reason not to celebrate. The more he tried to get to the main road, the more he wandered over small, obscure pathways.

In his wrath the driver cracked his whip on the backs of the horses, who broke out of control and began galloping wildly, pulling the carriage down curving lanes, racing as if possessed. Before the driver could stop them they had left the narrow road entirely and were heading straight into the dark forest.

"Stop!" he cried hoarsely, hitting them with all his strength. But anger brought on error, and the carriage began to totter between the trees. All his efforts to bring the horses under control met with failure.

"Leave the animals alone!" R' Baruch broke his silence, for the first time in hours. "With every crack of your whip you're breaking the Torah injunction against cruelty to animals."

His words pierced the man's heart. He waved his hands helplessly and let the horses go their own way.

In the blackness of night the carriage bumped through the tangle of trees in a forest that had no beginning and no end. A terrible sense of fear settled upon the passengers. A thick darkness fell; the gloominess of death surrounded them on all sides. Even the horses trembled in fear, froze in their places, and refused to budge.

The terrified passengers turned to R' Baruch. "What should we do?" they cried. They were terribly afraid that he would pay them back in the very words that they deserved: "And who got us into this mess after all?"

But no! R' Baruch spoke gently to them. "It is from Heaven that our carriage has come to these forgotten pathways; it is undoubtedly a purposeful plan of the One Who created the world. Cause and effect: The cause was your desire to crown me a leader upon you. But the effect? That is beyond my comprehension."

All through the night they sat, sleep eluding them. Fear of gangs of bandits lay heavily on their hearts, together with dread of wolf packs that might fall upon them, a hopeless group of unarmed men.

With the breaking of dawn they breathed a sigh of relief. They felt a pinprick of hope: Perhaps, in the light of day, they would find their way out of the forest. But they soon realized the error of their thinking. The trees were so high and thick they obscured all sunlight. Only a few lonely rays managed to pierce the thick foliage; here, there was no day and no night. "It's a miracle we have the wine and cakes," one said. "Otherwise, we might have starved to death."

"Some miracle," another said sarcastically. "If we hadn't been so clever as to take the rebbe against his will, we wouldn't be here at all!"

For two days the driver wandered through the forest. It seemed to the passengers that they were growing more and more lost. The baked goods were eaten joylessly, and soon gone; the wine was drunk dolefully, not bringing a smile to anyone. Some of the men began to wonder aloud if it was not time to begin preparing to stand before the Heavenly Court with repentance and good deeds.

Three days of fruitless wandering passed. Night fell. One of the passengers lit a stub of a candle and suggested that the driver make one final effort before giving up. The driver agreed and called to the horses, who began to make their way like blind men in a maze.

Suddenly the driver gave an excited yell. "I see light!"

The passengers looked out the windows of the coach, unbelieving. But the driver was right! Within the thick blackness a small light glimmered. When they grew closer they saw the light twinkling from a window in a small hut.

A debate broke out among the men: Should they approach the hut? But what if dangerous robbers were within?

They turned to R' Baruch, and with his approval they cautiously approached the hut. R' Baruch himself stayed inside the carriage.

Their fears disappeared when they saw a *mezuzah* on the doorway. Obviously, a G-d-fearing Jew lived here. They knocked and the door was immediately opened by an impressive-looking Jew, with a full beard and sparkling eyes.

The passengers wasted no time getting to the crux of the matter: "Reb Yid, how do we get out of here?"

The Jew was in no hurry. "What's the matter, gentlemen, what's the rush? Come inside, have something warm to drink, and then you will be on your way."

He stared out at the coach. The figure of R' Baruch could be seen peering out the half-open window.

"Are you all here? Who is left in the carriage?"

One of the *chassidim* quickly ran to the coach and brought the rebbe with him.

The Jew stared at his young guest's face and called out joyously, "Welcome the Rebbe, Reb Baruch'l. Welcome the Rebbe, Reb Baruch'l."

Everyone stood, rooted to the spot.

R' Baruch didn't lose his poise. "I have two questions for you. First, how do you know my name? You've never seen me before. And second, why do you call me 'the Rebbe'?"

"I was once able to do something for your grandfather, the holy *Besht*," the man answered. "Your grandfather wanted to return the favor. He called me to a room in his house and said to me, 'Would you like to see something phenomenal? Come, I'll show you.' He took me to a crib where a baby about one year old was sleeping. He commanded me to look at the baby's face, and said, 'Do you know who this little one is? He is my grandson — the Rebbe, Reb Baruch'l.'

"What can I tell you?" the owner of the hut continued. "I see your face now, and nothing has changed. Your face is exactly the same, the same holiness and innocence —"

R' Baruch and his *chassidim* accepted the reply. They thanked their strange host, bid him farewell, and once again boarded the carriage. A miracle, indeed: The horses immediately made their way to the main road. After a short ride the carriage left the forest behind and made its way towards Tulchin, with the rebbe, Reb Baruch'l, sitting within.

The Mohel in the Icy Wasteland

FROM THE DAY THAT THE LAW OF CONSCRIPTION CAME INTO effect in Poland, there was no rest for the holy Rebbe, R' Yehudah Aryeh Leib, the *Sefas Emes* of Gur.

Poland had for some years lain under the hobnailed boots of the Russian Czar, and had already shuddered beneath his heavy tread. There had been many difficult decrees, but this last was the worst.

There were several reasons that it was so terrible. The conscription was long, lasting for four full years in the Czar's army. The draftees were sent to forlorn places all over Russia. It was very difficult to observe the mitzvos while in the army, particularly the laws of *kashrus*. Frequently, soldiers faced the terrible choice of eating *tereifah* food or starving to death.

This decree was just the beginning of an even worse calamity: the Russo-Japanese War. The best of the country's youth were taken to battle; the cries of widows and women whose husbands had disappeared shattered the Rebbe's heart into bits. Ultimately, in the shadow of such troubles, the *Sefas Emes* fell ill with the last sickness that was to afflict him.

Day after day hundreds of 21-year-old men — draft age — came to the Rebbe's room, all sharing the same request: "Bless me, Rebbe, that I be exempt."

The Rebbe would give a loving look to the young people, men who should have been putting all their energies into their beloved Gemaras, being led like sheep to the slaughter. But their identical request would receive many different replies.

"Take the burden of Torah upon you," he would sometimes say. "We have learned that all who take the burden of Torah upon themselves are exempt from the burden of the State."

That was his answer to those average young men whose fate was in doubt. Whoever got that reply knew that he must work hard, pray and cry, accept the burden of Torah without wavering, serve his Creator, put in as much effort as he would had he been a soldier. And then perhaps, perhaps he would get his exemption — and perhaps not.

Then there were the lucky ones who heard the Rebbe's promise, swift and certain: "You have nothing to worry about. You won't have to go to the army."

There were three types of cards issued to those of draft age: a green card for conscripts, a white card for those exempt, and a blue card for yeshivah students who were given a one-year deferment.

For those fortunate enough to have received the Rebbe's blessing, the meeting before the draft board and subsequent exemption were nothing more than a symbolic act, making the Rebbe's decree official with the issuance of a white card.

Chaim Shlomo, a young Torah scholar, was one of the young *chassidim* who received the invitation to appear before the draft board. He was certain that the Rebbe would give him a blessing, ensuring his exemption. But it seemed that the Rebbe had accepted the decree. "It's as if he was waiting to hear my news," the thought flitted through Chaim Shlomo's head as he stood, trembling, before the holy man. The Rebbe confirmed his fears. There was no talk of exemptions. Instead, he told him tranquilly, "If you want to listen to me, you will become a *mohel.*"

"What did the Rebbe tell you?" Chaim Shlomo's worried friends asked him when he had left the Rebbe's room, his face ashen.

"It seems I'm to get a 'green card,'" he said brokenly. "I'm to be drafted."

"Why do you think such a terrible thing?"

"The Rebbe commanded me to learn to be a *mohel.*" The tears came of their own accord now. "Isn't that a clear hint?"

Chaim Shlomo's friends tried to calm him down and comfort him. "The Rebbe just meant to give you a means of supporting yourself." But Chaim Shlomo's heart understood the bitter tidings: "They'll be sending me to battle soon."

His friends realized that their words of comfort were pointless. The courtyard echoed with the grim words: "Chaim Shlomo is to be drafted."

The object of all the attention approached several expert *mohalim* and, with his quick and nimble hands, it wasn't long before he had learned the art of circumcision and was practicing like a veteran.

The train's wheels chugged along; The blast of the steam horn echoed through the air, clearing the way for the train racing from Warsaw on its way to Russia.

The railroad cars were jammed with hundreds of recruits in sparkling uniforms just out of the factory. Their crisp newness made a pleasant sound in the soldiers' ears. The air was lightly scented with the smell of fear mixed with burning steam from the powerful engine.

In the midst of this sea of humanity sat one figure completely different from the rest. A thick-bearded soldier leaned his head back upon his pack, which contained all of his possessions, and he gave a muffled sigh. He would have happily forgone the doubtful pleasure of being the lone Jewish soldier among this jumble of thousands of Russian and Polish recruits.

Twenty years of forging his soul within the flames of the Gerrer furnace marked him among the noisy flood, the sea of coarse faces. Strangers looked him up and down, scrutinized his every move with curious and taunting eyes, until he felt he would soon lose his wits. He longed to scream out, "Stupid gentiles, what are you staring at? I'm a Jew, a Jew!"

He could see images of the past days flit swiftly before him with feverish intensity: the draft order, the Rebbe's melancholy command to become a *mohel*, his appearance before the committee —

The words of the army physician still seared him like a flame. "Mr. Solomon," he said tauntingly, "I'm happy to tell you that you've been found fit to serve in His Majesty's army."

And then everything passed like a bad dream: the hastily packed luggage, a tearful farewell to the Rebbe, the *chassidim*, and to his family.

"Oh no!" Chaim Shlomo put his head in his hands. "My instruments!" Could he have actually left his precious instruments behind?

His hand feverishly sought through his pack. He gave a sigh of relief: Here was the knife, the bandages neatly rolled up in a small package, the metal container with its powders and medications —

The train's whistle announced an upcoming station.

"Where are we?" the passengers asked, their eyes still heavy with sleep.

"Everyone off immediately!" the officers shouted. "You've reached Paradise. One of these days you're going to long for this black hole!"

"Black?" the recruits wondered. "There's nothing here but white snow!"

"But they're right," one of the soldiers explained nastily. "When you're 2,000 miles from home, everything is black."

Deep in the icy wasteland, thousands of miles from civilization, the soldiers descended, trembling from the cold that seemed to cut their flesh like swords. They were settled within a huge army camp. No one had the slightest idea of what he was to do in this forgotten place: Officers muttered something about continuing the journey to the borders of Manchuria, near China, to the battlefields of the Russo-Japanese War, but it seemed that even they were not certain of anything.

They stayed in the camp awaiting orders.

The group was sitting in the dining room eating their tasteless army meal. A tall figure that entered the room caught the attention of the listless diners. The officer in charge jumped up respectfully and fearfully to greet the general, whose uniform glistened with medals.

The general motioned lightly with his finger. The officer quickly walked with him to a corner of the room. After a moment he returned to the soldiers, his face a mask of confusion.

"Is there a Jewish soldier here?" he asked hesitantly.

Hundreds of eyes turned towards Chaim Shlomo.

The officer took his arm with distinctly unmilitary gentleness. "Our esteemed guest, General Nikolai Fyodorov, wishes to speak with you."

Chaim Shlomo followed the general, who gestured to him to join him outside. A short and swift walk brought them to the edge of the camp. They stopped near the general's quarters.

"I have something confidential to tell you," the general said sternly. "But if you reveal a word of it —" The words he did not articulate could be clearly heard ripping threateningly through the frigid air.

"I am a believing Jew. You can have full faith in me," Chaim Shlomo declared ceremoniously.

"Okay, then," the general began, looking suspiciously around him.

The sound of wailing pierced the icy vastness. "You have a little boy," the army physician told General Fyodorov, the happy father.

The Jewish wife of the top officer shared his joy for only seven days. Her deceased father, who had been a G-d-fearing Jew in his life, had allowed his heavenly rest to be disturbed and had descended into her dreams. "Know, my daughter, that this son born to you is a Jew. You must circumcise him!"

The dream recurred night after night for several months. The general's wife almost lost her mind. How many times, after all, could a person see her dead father and remain sane? She beseeched her husband again and again, "You are a gentile but your son is a Jew. He must be circumcised!"

"And where am I to find a Jew in this frozen desert?" he would protest.

The argument began anew each day until today, when the wife had warned him, "If you can't find a Jew, don't bother coming back home!"

"And now that I've found you, do you know what to do?" The general pressed his fingers together, until the tips turned white.

Chaim Shlomo could hardly speak; his heart beat wildly inside. One moment's illumination, and suddenly everything was magically clear. All the shadows and the darkness, all the suffering and torture, all were destined just for this moment. To bring a child into the covenant of Avraham *Avinu*, here, at the very end of the earth —

"I am a professional *mohel*," the broken whisper, trembling with joy, barely came out of his dry throat.

The infant's cry of pain there in frozen Russia was obscured by the ecstatic weeping of the mother, who had finally merited to see her son circumcised. Remarkably, it even brought a sigh of pleasure to the gentile who was his father.

"What can I do to reward you?" the general asked, clearly moved.

"I don't need anything. I have but one request: Exempt me from the army," Chaim Shlomo answered. "I cannot keep my Torah in the army."

General Fyodorov was an important figure, and he used all his many connections for Chaim Shlomo's sake. After a short time the young *chassid* was free.

"There are times when a person must travel to the ends of the earth to help a Jewish soul," his rebbe, the *Sefas Emes,* explained after Chaim Shlomo had happily returned to the *chassidim* with his story of Jewish sacrifice. "Now you've done your duty as a soldier."

The Fruits of Tokay

The wagon wheels squeaked rhythmically with every turn. The rusty axles protested at being denied their rest in their old age, compelled to pull the carriage for such a long journey.

Inside, lying on pillows and blankets, Itche Dovid groaned. His energy had waned even before he had begun the long trip. The discordant rattle of a dry cough escaped from his chest. It was followed by another cough, and another. Droplets of blood issuing from infected lungs bubbled up, coloring his pale lips a bright scarlet.

"Oh, Father in Heaven, sweet Father, when will we finally reach Tokay?" he thought for the thousandth time.

"Patience, Reb Itche Dovid," the carriage driver called out as if reading his thoughts. "A few more days and we'll be crossing the Hungarian border."

"I've heard that song now for two weeks." The terrible pains in his chest hadn't taken away his good cheer; he still could joke lightly.

He again took his *Mishnayos* in his hands, delving into a complicated *mishnah.* Here, with this *sefer,* it was he who was in control, not his illness! Tuberculosis was destroying his lungs daily — but he had so much more Torah to learn!

He tired quickly. His entire body, it seemed, was being consumed, together with his stricken lungs. Slowly his eyes closed.

The monotonous squeaking of the wagon wheels seemed to slice through his brain like a saber. As he lay half-asleep, the memories began to dance before him, pulling him back, to faraway Stolin.

Itche Dovid had never envisioned becoming a *shochet*. Even as a child he had been studious, engrossed in his learning, concentrating only on the *Masechta* being discussed. A deep spiritual hunger consumed him, only to be satisfied with still another page of Gemara, and another page, and another. This spiritual hunger included a craving to serve his Creator; he fed it in the court of the great rebbe, R' Aharon of Karlin, the author of the *Beis Aharon*.

R' Aharon's son, R' Asher, had been named his heir, and was acclaimed throughout the court. R' Asher was completely removed from worldly affairs; only the most fragile of bonds connected him to this earth. His soul seemed to desire only to go up to its Father in Heaven. And so it was: Only a little more than a year after the death of his father, the *Beis Aharon,* R' Asher gave his life for the sake of his brothers. During a plague in the city of Derohovitch, a plague that left large numbers dead, R' Asher chose to be the atonement for the rest of his people: He grew ill and died in Derohovitch — and the plague came to an end!

No one had ever seen R' Asher enjoy a big meal; indeed, he seemed uninterested in a poor repast as well. He would eat his small share of bread, and would not touch meat or chicken for long periods of time. The young man's skin was translucent, and his veins stood out in relief like markings on a map. His bones protruded frighteningly. His frailty worried his pious mother, Rebbetzin Chava, wife of the *Beis Aharon*, who begged him not to abuse his body and to eat something in order to strengthen himself, lest his soul abandon his body before its time.

"Why shouldn't you have a bit of meat or chicken?" she beseeched him. "Or if you refuse meat, what about a little soup?"

Once, he could not ignore the pleas of his mother's worried, loving heart.

"Do you know our Itche Dovid?" he said. "If he were the *shochet*, I would eat of his meat with confidence."

"But Itche Dovid sits and learns. He's not a *shochet*."

"I didn't say he should become one. I simply meant that if a man steeped in holiness and awe such as Itche Dovid were the *shochet*, I could eat meat."

The rebbetzin mentioned this to one of the *chassidim*.

The next day the students banded together to speak to Itche Dovid.

"Why don't you learn to be a *shochet*?" They threw the request, which had the sound of an order, before him, as they relayed to him what R' Asher had said of him.

Itche Dovid tried to wriggle free. "I'm only interested in Torah! Are you prepared to take the responsibility for tearing me away from learning?"

But the men wouldn't leave him. "And you? Will you take responsibility for R' Asher's life? If you become a *shochet*, you will have saved a Jewish soul!"

The debate raged. Finally after many hours, Itche Dovid did what they demanded of him: He agreed to become a *shochet*.

And when a man such as Itche Dovid becomes a *shochet* he does it with awe and reverence; he does it with his entire being. In sanctity and fear he learned the trade, its every detail. He delved deeply into the laws of *shechitah* as outlined in the *Shulchan Aruch,* and he took his apprenticeship in the slaughterhouse. It did not take long for Itche Dovid to have learned the trade in depth. He was tested and found deserving of being named a *shochet* of the first rank. The good news was brought to R' Asher, and on those infrequent occasions when he was ready to eat meat, Itche Dovid was immediately called upon.

Itche Dovid was a good student; perhaps too good. The student began to teach the teacher. When he stood behind the *shochtim* at the slaughterhouse he was not satisfied with their means of whetting their knives. "That's how you sharpen your knives?" His voice was critical. He took a knife in his hand and began to run it onto the whetstone back and forth, up and down, again and again. Sparks flew from beneath his swiftly moving hands.

"You don't need to do it so much!" Another *shochet* stopped him, mockingly. "I won't have a knife left by the time you're done!"

When Itche Dovid was studying, the *shochtim* wouldn't allow him to sharpen the knives. But when he became R' Asher's private *shochet* he bought a few whetstones for himself. He prayed often, with tears running down his cheeks, that he should not bring the great man to sin by *shechitah* that was not in perfect accord with the halachah. But more than his prayers were his efforts prior to, during, and after the *shechitah* itself.

Before the *shechitah* he would take the knife out of the leather sheath where it lay like an *esrog* lovingly covered with flax. With awe and trepidation he would take the knife to the whetstone and begin to sharpen it with movements so swift one could not see his hands clearly. The sharp metal hitting the rock gave off sparks of dust into his face. His stones would become worn down at a dizzying rate; jokers used to say that Itche Dovid didn't slaughter chickens, he slaughtered stones.

During the *shechitah* Itche Dovid would grab the chicken by its wings and give it a complete "eight-fold inspection": the tendons and sinews, the neck, the joints, the feet. He would close his eyes and fervently recite the blessing, his whole body shaking. Then, with lightning swiftness, he would pass his knife over the neck. Before the bird had an inkling of what was happening to it, it had been slaughtered.

After the *shechitah* he would open the chicken and inspect the lungs and all other parts that needed to be checked. He would take a last good look at the entire chicken and finally pronounce the word "kosher" over it.

How happy Itche Dovid was when R' Asher ate the chicken he had slaughtered. All the effort seemed worthwhile for this moment. The holy Rebbe, whose sensitive mouth could not swallow meat slaughtered by someone who had not reached an incredibly high level of reverence of G-d, began to eat meat now, after such a long period of abstinence!

Itche Dovid, in his satisfaction and enthusiasm, began to be even more careful in his preparations for slaughtering. He would sharpen the knife endlessly. The sweat would pour down from his face as he stood over the whetstone, and the room would be full of thick dust.

This dust settled in his lungs, dropping layer after layer upon them. The diligent *shochet's* body was wracked with terrible coughing, but that did not deter him from his careful ways.

Time passed. The young rebbe, R' Asher of Karlin-Stolin, was taken during the plague of Derohovitch. Over the course of years Itche Dovid gained the reputation as a sterling and unmatched *shochet*, and his services were in great demand. Endless numbers of chickens were slaughtered — and endless numbers of whetstones ground down — by the diligent *shochet*. And the dust flew and settled, and his lungs became covered until there was no room left to breathe.

When Itche Dovid was stricken with a choking cough, his worried family brought him to specialists in the area. These doctors threw up their hands helplessly and sent him on to Warsaw. Perhaps someone there could find a cure.

The specialist in the Warsaw hospital completed his intensive examination. He, too, lifted his hands in despair and, sighing, told the family, "He's got no lungs left. They are not lungs at all, they're just liquid!"

At that moment Itche Dovid felt that his heart, too, had turned to water. The specialist was saying that he had no chance to live! His face paled like a dead man's. But then he heard the specialist continue speaking.

"The patient has just one small chance, and a very small chance at that. And yet, even a small possibility of life is better than certain death."

The family listened intently, to ensure that they didn't miss a word.

"In Hungary there is a small city, a city of vineyards, called

Tokay. The city is entirely surrounded by the best quality vines, whose product, as you know, becomes Tokay wine, renowned throughout the entire world.

"We send the worst pulmonary cases to Tokay, where the air is pleasant and sweet from the scent of the vineyards. The sick men breathe the clear, fragrant air of the city and sometimes it helps their illness.

"You'll have to weigh the risks against the benefits," the doctor concluded in a warning tone. "On the one hand, there is indeed a small chance for him there. On the other, the journey is long and difficult, particularly for someone as sick as he is. You should be aware of what you are taking upon yourselves."

Itche Dovid woke from his twilight nap. The wagon had made good time these past days. The steep, hilly rises had given way to flat ground and the horses seemed to have grown wings. Their hooves were swift and they covered twice the distance in half the time.

A purplish sun was disappearing over the western plain, casting the entire horizon in orange-red flame. "Another few hours and we reach Tokay," the driver informed his passenger after looking carefully around him.

Evening arrived. The dimness of twilight passed into the darkness of night. By the flickering light of a lantern the horses plodded on patiently, carefully feeling their way.

A sweet fragrance began to fill the air. The driver halted the horses and wiped his brow. He filled his lungs with the unique air that could not be mistaken for any other. Yes, this was the wonderful air of Tokay. The clear scent of grapes grew even clearer as they drew nearer to the city.

"Itche Dovid, come and get up," the driver called out cheerily. "We've reached Tokay."

A thick fog covered the city. The horses wandered through the streets, while the driver and his sick passenger kept a sharp lookout for a house with a candle still burning in its window. In vain: It was very late and all the inhabitants were fast asleep.

"Do you have somewhere to go?" The wagoner's question went unanswered; like the driver, Itche Dovid knew no one in this strange city.

"What should we do?" the driver reiterated his question. "Where should we go?"

"Take me to the local *hekdesh* (the Jews' guest house)," Itche Dovid said weakly.

The loud knocking on the door of the *hekdesh* awakened the caretaker, Yaakov Meir, from his deep sleep.

"Who's that knocking at 2 o'clock in the morning?" he bellowed, as he turned over in his bed. The sound of a hail of blows falling upon the wooden portal convinced him that he was not dreaming. Slowly he shuffled toward the door, opening it just a crack.

"Who are you?" he asked, his voice thick with sleep.

"Open the door," the wagoner demanded. "I've brought you a guest from Lithuania."

"What?" the caretaker rolled his eyes. "Not even King Achashverosh would get a bed here at this hour!"

The driver impatiently explained the urgency of this night appearance. "And now I'm giving you the responsibility of taking care of this sick man. I've done my job."

Clearly reluctant, Yaakov Meir put on his overcoat and went outside. The two of them, the driver and the caretaker, lifted the sick man out of the wagon and laid him down in a far corner of the *hekdesh*. Among the peddlers, the small-time merchants who traveled from town to town, and other wandering guests who lay deeply asleep, some on the bare floor and others on ragged mats, they found an empty space for "the Lithuanian."

The caretaker returned to his own bed, which was no more than a collection of branches and twigs that could hardly be called a mattress. He settled himself carefully on it and immediately began snoring lightly.

When he heard more knocking — recognizable, if not welcome — coming from the entrance to the door and once again pulling him from his comfortable repose, he was furious.

"Now I'll just refuse to open it," he told himself. "I'll show him!"

The knocking grew louder and more urgent. "Open the door!" someone shouted.

For a moment, a curse came to the caretaker's lips. His fury knew no bounds. Had you ever heard of such a thing? What did that crazy wagoner from Lithuania want from him?

"Yaakov Meir, open the door!" someone shouted sternly. "It's me, Zussman!"

Yaakov Meir shuddered. That voice was unmistakable: the voice of R' Zussman Farkash, mayor of the Jewish community of Tokay!

Yaakov Meir was at the doorway in an instant. He pulled at the squeaky lock that he'd bolted shut not long before.

"And what does the honorable mayor want?" he asked humbly. The mayor was the boss of Tokay; his hands firmly gripped all the reins of power in the city. If he wanted, he could have Yaakov Meir fired without blinking an eye.

"Has someone from Stolin come here?"

"No one." Yaakov Meir had never heard of the town.

"Impossible." The mayor was adamant. "Didn't they bring you a sick man just before?"

The caretaker slapped his brow with the palm of his hand. "Of course. But he's from Lithuania."

The mayor was in a hurry; this was no time for a geography lesson. "Take me to him."

In the light of a flickering candle Zussman carefully scrutinized Itche Dovid's face as he lay on the floor. "That's him," he muttered to himself. The sick man half-opened his eyes.

"Have you come here from Stolin?"

Itche Dovid nodded his head, yes.

"Did you know the young Rebbe of Stolin?"

A spark glistened in the dark eyes. "I was near him until his death."

The mayor wouldn't let up. "Describe him to me."

Itche Dovid enthusiastically described the unusual figure of the Rebbe. Zussman nodded his head, as cold shivers struck him on the warm summer night.

"You will come with me," he finally said. "Yaakov Meir, help me bring this man to my house."

Itche Dovid didn't know if what happened next was just part of his dreams, or if it really took place. Yaakov Meir, too, kept rubbing at his eyes, unbelieving. The mayor of Tokay, feared by all of his townspeople, set to work like a common laborer. Zussman whistled and a few helpers who had been waiting for him in his elegant coach came running. Itche Dovid's possessions, that had just been unpacked, were gathered together again and loaded onto the carriage; Itche Dovid followed, brought out on a stretcher.

The procession reached the mayor's luxurious home, still steeped in blackness. The mayor lit dozens of wax candles in their special brass candlesticks, bringing precious light into all the rooms.

Itche Dovid was taken by the servants to the elegant parlor. His clothing, reeking of the dirt of travel, was changed for a clean robe. The mayor himself supervised the sick man's bath and made certain he lacked for nothing.

In a soft and comfortable bed, the likes of which he had never enjoyed, Itche Dovid lay, covered with a woolen blanket, his head propped onto down pillows. He hardly knew who he was. In his own impoverished home he was accustomed to taking a quick nap on a twig-filled mat covered with thin flaxen cloth, a mat that had known better days in the home of its first owner. Pillows, blankets — these were the stuff of dreams.

Itche Dovid longed to find out what was happening but was embarrassed to ask his benefactor why he was working so diligently for his benefit when he had never met him. He did not even know his name, except that he'd heard the man's wife call him Zussman.

The sunlight washed through the room. Itche Dovid awoke and saw the mayor standing at his bedside. In one hand he held a cup and in the other an ewer of water. First, he helped his guest wash his hands. Zussman Farkash then helped him wind the straps of his *tefillin* around his arm, and held the *siddur* before him, turning page after page. Itche Dovid had never experienced such paternal hospitality in his life.

"As if I were the rebbe and he were the assistant," The thought flickered through the sick man's mind. "But why? Why does he seem to tremble before me?"

After morning prayers his host disappeared, but several servants entered bearing trays of delicacies.

"Breakfast is very important, particularly for someone who is not well," one of them explained as he poured out a fragrant cup of tea into a fragile cup.

He was still savoring a fresh pastry when Zussman reentered the room. He immediately flung the windows open.

"Every minute that goes by without you breathing in this air is simply a waste of time. Isn't this the reason you came to Tokay?"

As he spoke Zussman clapped his hands. One of the servants entered carrying a basket full of many-hued purple grapes wrapped in green leaves. Itche Dovid had never seen such huge fruits. The servant placed bunches of grapes on all the windowsills. An intoxicating scent immediately wafted through the entire room; the sick man felt pleasantly dizzy from it.

Itche Dovid's silent look seemed to plead with his host: "Please, let me know why you're doing all this for me."

Zussman Farkash had not been chosen mayor of Tokay for his stupidity. He returned Itche Dovid's look with one of his own, one that promised: "Time will tell; you will soon know why I tremble before you."

A few weeks passed. Zussman hardly moved from Itche Dovid's bedside. He fed him with his own hands. He often sent his servants away, preferring to take care of his guest by himself. Every day he made sure that fresh grapes were picked and brought to the room, to bring in their strong healthy scent.

The devoted treatment elicited results: Itche Dovid started to feel markedly better. He still would occasionally spit up blood and his body would sometimes be wracked by coughing that seemed to stab at him like a sharp knife. Still, he could tell that there was no comparison between his condition now and the way he had felt when he had first been brought to his benefactor's home.

One morning, the elegant coach of the mayor stood before the house. Inside, the seats were covered with soft blankets. The whinnying of the horses in the courtyard brought a questioning look to Itche Dovid's eyes, but he said nothing. Though he had been here for quite a while, he had hardly opened his mouth. In these days he felt in his own life the words of the Sages: Whoever eats the bread of his friend's charity is ashamed to look him in the face (*Tosafos, Kiddushin* 36b).

"Up until now the grapes have been brought to Itche Dovid; from now on, Itche Dovid will be brought to them." Zussman Farkash was feeling cheerful, as he supported his guest and helped him into the coach. "Reb Yid, you're already halfway healthy, so you may now travel to the famous vineyards of Tokay. No more lying in bed waiting for the grapes to come to your window."

The horses trotted gently towards the outskirts of the city. If Itche Dovid had thought that he had fully experienced the scents of Tokay, he now found out how mistaken he had been. The enchanting fragrance of the vineyards permeated the air, filling his lungs with such force that he felt he would faint.

"Look out of the window and watch," Zussman held his guest's wrists, terrified that he would collapse. Perhaps he had been too hasty; maybe the patient had not recovered enough and this first encounter with the vineyards would harm rather than help him.

His face white, Itche Dovid turned towards the window in the coach. The scene before him left him speechless. He gazed at row after row of ripe grapes, endlessly stretching with no beginning and no end, east to west, north to south. He tried to see the horizon, make out where the rows began, find one corner without vines, but he did not succeed.

"These are the famed vineyards of Tokay. From here comes wine known throughout the world. In another few weeks all the grapes will have ripened completely and the harvest will begin. We won't be able to come here during that time, when thousands of workers will be passing among the rows." The mayor's voice was full with obvious pride. "I suspect I'm correct in assuming you've never seen anything like this in your life."

Itche Dovid nodded his head in assent. The two descended from the carriage and wandered through the rows of grapes for a long while, breathing deeply of the intoxicating fragrance.

From that day on, the trip to the vineyards became a regular event. In the twilight hours the two would walk together, enjoying deep conversation. They became very close. The mayor grew to know Itche Dovid, the lofty and elevated man, rather than the pitiful and hopeless invalid whom he was helping to heal. Itche Dovid, too, felt a closeness towards his host.

One day, he finally dared bring up the question that had been nagging at him since he'd met the mayor. "Why? Why the incredible devotion to a stranger from a faraway land?"

The mayor immediately sunk into himself like a snail hiding in its shell. He would only say one sentence from between sealed lips: "The day is not far away when you'll know everything, and understand everything!"

"I can't keep it to myself any longer. I've got to tell you everything." Zussman Farkash burst into Itche Dovid's room one morning like a stormy wind. "I've been keeping it to myself for months, using all my strength not to tell you, because it would excite you too much. But now, it is time!"

The mayor sat on a chair next to Itche Dovid. His words carried Itche Dovid right back to the days of his youth.

On that strange night, Zussman Farkash had an unforgettable dream. An elegant, fine-looking man came to him and asked, "Are you Zussman Farkash, mayor of Tokay?"

"Yes I am," he answered humbly.

"I am the Rebbe of Stolin. I have disturbed my rest in the land of souls to come here on behalf of my devoted *chassid*, Itche Dovid."

The voice, then, came from the World of Judgment.

"He was devoted to me when I was alive. His name is Itche Dovid, and he sacrificed his life for me. He became a *shochet* just so that I could eat meat. In his great concern for halachah he endangered himself, and he is now mortally ill with tuberculosis. I appreciate what he's done for me and feel obligated to take care of him. He's just been brought to the *hekdesh*. Get up and bring him to your home."

"How will I know how the man looks?" the mayor asked.

The Rebbe of Stolin described his looks in detail.

"The mitzvah that you will do is a great one. Though you don't need a reason to do it, know, then, that the one who orders it is faithful and will pay you well."

"And he will —" Zussman could hardly breathe.

"For many years you have been childless, haven't you? To reward you, you and your spouse will have a child to hold in your arms."

Zussman shook his head, as one trying to shake off the chains of sleep. The memory of the dream had touched him deeply; it was as if the dream had tried to jump into his world and become reality.

In the darkness he could feel a pair of eyes staring at him.

"What's happened, dear?"

"I had a strange dream," his wife said to him, her voice trembling. "A holy man came to me in a vision."

The two sat up and told each other their dreams, realizing almost immediately that they had each had the identical vision!

"This is a sign that the dream is true, and not just some fantasy," Zussman said excitedly. "But let me prove that this isn't just foolishness. I'm going to the *hekdesh!*"

"Now? In the middle of the night? Can't you wait until morning?" his wife tried to talk him out of his mad plan.

"If a mitzvah comes to you, don't put it off," Zussman quoted, and he immediately left to the *hekdesh*.

"If you remember how I stood over you that night, looking at your face," Zussman was deeply involved in his story, and did not notice Itche Dovid's face, that had grown as white as newly fallen snow, "you can now completely understand why I was examining you so carefully. The more I stared the more I saw the details of the description your Rebbe had given me from the higher world, a description that could match no other man. And when you described the Rebbe of Stolin, I was more convinced than ever that this dream was one of those of which it is said, 'one sixtieth of them is prophecy.' "

"And why today?" Itche Dovid was a man of great faith, and yet his heart thumped wildly at the effort to believe such things.

"Oh," the mayor gave a satisfied sigh — he'd saved this treat for last — "I am a messenger today. Today we've found out for certain that the blessing your Rebbe gave to us will soon take place. G-d has already helped us!"

A few more months passed. Itche Dovid felt like a new man. The disease had disappeared without a trace. The cough had quieted, the pains vanished and belonged to the past. With the consent of local physicians he decided it was time to return home.

Zussman Farkash escorted him to the train station.

"In my opinion you can go home directly, but I suppose you should go hear what the doctors in Warsaw have to say."

The journey to Warsaw became an opportunity to advertise the miracle. The *kiddush Hashem* began in the office of the Warsaw specialist. The doctor had not forgotten the dying man.

"A miracle! A miracle! It's unbelievable!" he cried out in amazement after examining Itche Dovid. "When you visited me I didn't think you'd last much longer; you had no lungs left at all! I didn't really think that Tokay would help you, but it actually built you a new pair of lungs!"

When they heard his raised voice other doctors in the hospital came to see what was happening. Many remembered the young man who had come to their hospital with destroyed lungs. They could hardly believe what they saw now. "There is indeed a G-d in Israel," they said with feeling.

⌒∽◯◡⌒

Itche Dovid's reception at home would be long remembered. His friends and neighbors flocked to his house; for hours he repeated his amazing story.

When the last of the guests had left, he turned to his wife. "I have something important to ask you. Tell me the truth — while I've been away, how have you managed? Who has supported you this whole time?"

His wife left the room for a moment, and returned with a sheaf of envelopes in her hand.

"A few weeks after you left, I began to get mail from Hungary. A man whose name I didn't recognize sent me a large sum of money every month. I had more than enough to feed and clothe the children."

Itche Dovid looked at the envelope and stared at the return address. During his year in Tokay he had learned to read a little of the local language.

"Zussman Farkash, mayor, Tokay."

The Doctor of Belz

NO ONE COULD HAVE BEEN MORE UPSET THAN R' Yehoshua Kestenbaum as he took leave of his teacher and Rebbe, the *tzaddik* R' Sar-Shalom of Belz.

"Ten years I've been close to the holy Rebbe," he told his friends after he had received his Rebbe's farewell blessing. "I was like Adam *HaRishon* in the Garden of Eden, being served meat and poured wine by angels of heaven. Who would have believed that the day would come when I would be exiled?"

Shortly before this R' Sar-Shalom had commanded his faithful *chassid*, Yehoshua, to leave Belz and travel to Russia. The Rebbe's reasons were hidden from the *chassid*, and though he knew the Rebbe meant only for his good, abandoning the court was hard, terribly hard. He felt like R' Tarfon, when he told R' Akiva, "Akiva, whoever leaves you leaves life."

Yehoshua and his family faced a long and arduous journey from Galicia to the depths of Russia, traveling part way by boat, part by train, and the remainder by horse-drawn coach.

Two months after he left his Rebbe and his friends in Belz, he settled into a small and remote Russian town, a sparsely settled city which was home to the Graf, a noble who was lord of several neighboring villages.

Yehoshua made the acquaintance of the Graf and his household. He impressed the nobleman with his wisdom. Soon the Graf was showing him signs of favor, and eventually he granted him the rights to lease the local inn and bar, as well as fields and orchards, to the mutual satisfaction of both parties. Yehoshua's rental fees were fair, and he built a substantial and stable business. All day he stood and served the gentile customers; in the evening, when his energy waned, he would tiredly walk to the *beis midrash*, sit down wearily on a bench, and listen, half-asleep, to a *shiur* in *Mishnayos*.

During those first days of his new-found life, Yehoshua's longing for the holy court of Belz was so strong he thought he would go mad. Instead of Torah learning from morning to night, here he was pouring vodka down the throats of drunken gentiles! Instead of dwelling in G-d's home, he was living in the tents of strangers!

But time works its miracles. The sun rises and sets and the globe travels in its orbit. A year, two years, and Yehoshua, though broken-hearted, grew accustomed to his life in the forlorn Russian town.

His relations with the Graf, owner of the bar and inn, were excellent. The Graf would often speak with the clever Jew who seemed, no less than the educated and enlightened noble himself, so familiar with the ways of the world.

Yehoshua became acquainted with Gregory, the Graf's eldest son, a bright young man who was his father's pride and joy. Though he was only 15 years old, he had unusual talents and Gregory's father was already preparing him for the great university in Petersburg.

The Graf rejoiced in his young son and bragged of him to all. The youngster, whose reading had not included "The Gate of Modesty" in *Sefer Orchos Tzaddikim,* was also full of himself and his importance, and took every opportunity to show off his wit and wisdom. The Graf's visitors, family, and many friends were often told of his illustrious son, assured that the boy would become either a professor or a minister, if not something even greater.

The Graf made one terrible error: He constantly and impatient-ly pushed his son to show off his rapid development in his studies. Gregory began to believe that his father would love him only if he were the best in everything. He tried very hard, but because of the enormous pressure, and the fear that he would lose his parent's esteem if he wouldn't prove himself daily, his mind began to weak-en. It did not take long for the promising young man to become certifiably mad, acting insane both in private and in public.

The Graf did not know what to do with his humiliation and shame. Not only had his son not fulfilled his early promise, but he was not even like an average person. The grieving father locked him in a room in one of the wings of his sprawling castle and hoped that no one outside would hear the terrible cries from with-in its thick walls.

When Yehoshua came to visit the Graf he was shocked to see his grim appearance. At first the Graf was reluctant to reveal what was troubling him, but after Yehoshua pleaded with him he told him all that had happened.

"Has he seen a doctor?" Yehoshua asked.

"A doctor?" the Graf gave a bitter sigh. "I've consulted with doctor after doctor, and nothing has helped. I've even tried psychics and exorcists, and they've come up with nothing! My son, Gregory, the genius, has gone mad!"

With these words, the Graf's voice broke and he burst into tears that sent shivers through Yehoshua's merciful heart. He sank into a reverie, remembering how the Rebbe, Sar-Shalom of Belz, used to deal with the insane.

"Do you know what?" he told the weeping nobleman. "Before I came here, I lived in faraway Belz, where I sat in the shadow of a great rabbi, a holy man of G-d, who knew how to cure madmen like your son."

A spark of hope flickered in the Graf's despairing eyes. "What did you say?" He grabbed his hand like a drowning man grasping a straw. "You know someone who has healed people like my son?"

"Dozens of times," Yehoshua answered in confident tones. "With my own eyes I saw how they would bring certified lunatics, who spoke and behaved like complete madmen, and the Rebbe would cure them with a short conversation. Many left his room as sane as any other man."

"So what are we waiting for?" the Graf shouted eagerly. "We must leave for that small village as soon as possible!"

The Graf's use of the word "we" convinced Yehoshua that his heart's dream was about to come true: The Graf would take him along on the journey to Belz, the town Yehoshua longed for constantly. The salvation of the Graf would prove to be the *chassid's* deliverance as well, from the terrible stirrings of homesickness.

After a few days of preparations, a coach left the city. Inside sat three passengers: Yehoshua, the Graf, and his son, Gregory, the young man gone mad.

～♪♫～

Yehoshua's happiness when he shook the hand of his teacher and Rebbe, R' Sar-Shalom of Belz, was indescribable. All the longing that he had concealed in his heart burst forth in that handshake. His heart was filled with rapturous joy even while tears streamed down his face.

After their greeting the Rebbe asked him, "What are you doing here? Didn't I send you to Russia?"

Yehoshua told him all that had happened, including the story of the Graf's son. "Rebbe, it will be a tremendous *kiddush Hashem* if the Rebbe will heal the mad son of the Graf, as he has healed so many hundreds of our people," he concluded. "A gentile ruler, a man of influence, will see that there is a G-d in Israel!"

But R' Sar-Shalom wasn't impressed with his *chassid's* fervent words. "It's not enough that I bother Heaven for the benefit of the Jewish people, you want to force me to change nature for the sake of healing a mad gentile?"

Yehoshua left his Rebbe like one who had been slapped in the face. He knew how the Graf had hoped to reach Belz, because of the stories that he, Yehoshua, had told him, of the miracles the Rebbe had worked. How could he face the Graf now, and what would he tell him?

The Graf was waiting anxiously in the large lobby of his luxurious hotel in the gentile section of the city. Impatiently he walked back and forth, awaiting the return of "his" Jew.

When he heard Yehoshua's footsteps he jumped up and opened the door. "What did your rabbi say? Has he called for my son?" he asked breathlessly.

Yehoshua's face was crestfallen. In a low voice he tried to evade the question but the Graf would not let him go until he revealed the entire, unadorned truth.

When he heard what the rabbi had said, the Graf's face turned scarlet in fury. Angrily, he shouted, "He can help me, but he doesn't want to because I'm not of his religion? I'll show him! Three hundred Jews work for me in my villages and towns, throughout the region. I'll throw them all out! Every one of them, children and old men alike!" His furious voice echoed through the room like distant thunder. "And I'll begin with you, Yehoshua," he continued wrathfully. "You will not set foot in my coach, and when you return in a plain carriage, your wife and children, weeping and wailing in exile, will be there to meet you!"

When Yehoshua saw that disaster had struck he raced like a stricken deer directly to his Rebbe.

"Help me, for I'm doomed," he called out bitterly as he had his second audience with the Rebbe. "Three hundred families will have to take up the wanderer's staff because the Rebbe refuses to help one gentile?"

When the Rebbe heard that the multitudes faced dreadful suffering, and that the gentile, his wishes unfulfilled, was driven to punishment and violence, he immediately changed his mind. "Go back to your master and tell him his son will be healed."

Yehoshua's face brightened. He wanted to race out to the Graf and tell him the good news, but R' Sar-Shalom stopped him. "Slow down. Go back safely to your city. On the way, count the villages that you pass. When you come to the seventh village, go to the home of the local priest. He will cure the Graf's son."

Yehoshua saw the change in the Graf even before he had a chance to open his mouth with the news. The Graf had been hearing, from his hosts, a little of the great power wielded by the Rebbe, R' Sar-Shalom, in general matters and particularly in the cure of the mad. He firmly believed that whatever the Rebbe said would come true.

They sat glued to the window of the coach, staring at the fields passing them by. Each village and settlement that they passed was carefully counted off, as if heralding the cure that was to come.

"This is the seventh village!" the Graf yelled excitedly when he saw a few small homes growing larger on the horizon.

"Just a little while longer and your son will be healed," Yehoshua said happily, sneaking a glance at Gregory, who was lying on the coach's leather seat, a dribble of saliva trickling out of his mouth, his eyes staring blankly and his lips moving wordlessly.

And yet, when they descended the coach and took Gregory to the priest's home, the *chassid* found himself filled with fear. This specific priest was well known for his wickedness, an anti-Semite of Amalekite proportions. Yehoshua remembered him well from earlier days, recalling how so many Jews had come to the Rebbe R' Sar-Shalom to lament over the troubles this priest had caused them. The Rebbe's assurance that help would come specifically from this evil priest was beyond his comprehension.

◁○▷

The priest, shocked, didn't believe what he was hearing. "What did you say?" he asked the Graf and Yehoshua angrily.

The Graf didn't understand the priest's display of temper. "His rabbi," he said, pointing at Yehoshua, who was trembling in fright, "sent us here from his home in Belz, so that you could heal my son from his insanity," he repeated.

And at that moment, like a match thrown into a barrel full of gunpowder, the priest exploded. He shouted and cursed like one possessed. His eyes grew wide and his face turned a bright red as he cursed Yehoshua and all his fellow Jews, their rabbis, and their Torah. In his wrath he turned his face skyward and began to babble. Froth bubbled on his lips; his eyes grew mad.

"I don't have enough lunatics to deal with?" the Graf muttered to Yehoshua. "Let's get out of here."

And lo! A miracle! Before the eyes of the Graf and Yehoshua it happened: Just as the priest began to rant and rave, dancing and jumping and screaming like a veteran lunatic, Gregory looked at them with eyes full of intelligence and understanding, like a man in perfect health.

The sickness had left the boy — and entered the priest!

The Graf tested his son, spoke to him, asked him questions and heard his sane, clear replies. His understanding had returned. His words were thought out, intelligent, as if he had never been ill.

It is said that three men returned to Belz, where the Graf gave generous donations to all those Jews who sat and learned, outfitting them in beautiful clothing. And from that day on he became a righteous gentile, showing much favor to all the Jews who lived in his province.

To Give Up Everything

JAN PETROVSKI, THE HEAD OF THE VILLAGE, TURNED TO the Jewish innkeeper, R' Yosef, and whispered in his ear, "I have something private to discuss with you."

For many years, R' Yosef, an upright and pious man, had been paying rent to Petrovski. The years had been good to both of them: R' Yosef had earned a fine living from his inn, and the landlord had never had cause for complaint against his "Mushke," as he called him, who always paid his rent promptly.

R' Yosef was now standing in the landlord's home, waiting to hear what his master had to say.

"To my great sorrow, I am forced to say farewell and leave the village. I've been offered a huge estate in Moldavia, and my wife is driving me mad. Ever since she heard of this offer she's given me no peace. She knows only one sentence: Let's go to Moldavia, to that marvelous country with its rivers and magical scenery. And so — we're going!"

R' Yosef stood before him, shocked by the unexpected news.

"Mushke," the landlord continued, "you know that I like you very much. I want you to become the new head of the village."

R' Yosef's head whirled; he felt as if someone had hit him hard. He, the tenant, with his small business and his constant battle to meet the rental payments, should become head of the entire village?

For a few moments he stood, motionless and speechless. Then he recovered.

"My dear, good landlord," he said, his voice trembling, "I could never get enough money together to pay for the entire village!"

"I know, my son, I know," the landlord said affectionately. "But I've decided that I don't want to give up this village to any of the other landlords in the area. I want you to buy it, even for only a tenth of its value!"

Again, the Jew wondered if this was real or merely a dream. But the landlord would not relent. "Come back to me in a few days. In exchange for some ready cash, I'll give you the entire village!"

R' Yosef walked to his house, his mind reeling. It was hard for him to adjust to the incredible turnabout: the innkeeper to become the master of the village? Without any effort or work he would become such a wealthy man — And yet his heart sank when he realized he did not know how to put together even the few hundred rubles — a tenth of the market price — that the landlord had requested. And then his eyes lit up: "A woman is granted greater insight than a man," he thought. "Let me ask my wife."

When his wife heard his news, she, too, was stunned. But soon she was doing the reckoning.

"We've got the money!" she announced joyfully.

R' Yosef stared at her in wonder.

"Look around you. Your house belongs to you, all of the furniture, the silver and gold, the jewelry and candlesticks. We'll sell everything for cash; it will certainly add up to a few hundred rubles."

"And if not?" R' Yosef asked her with a glance.

"There are still fine people in the world," she answered, correctly interpreting his look. "We'll borrow from our friends and neighbors. We can't turn down this great favor that G-d has bestowed upon us!"

Soon the news was all over town: R' Yosef, the innkeeper, is selling all he owns. Within a few days he had sold his house and his possessions, and he had raised the entire amount needed, without having to take a single loan.

Joyously he walked to the landlord's house, his hands eagerly clutching the sack that contained his little fortune of several hundred rubles. All this time he had not stopped thinking about the incredible change in his life that was about to take place. He still could not comprehend the happiness and wealth that were to be his so suddenly.

"Woe!"

A terrible cry followed by bitter wailing shattered the silence and broke right through to the depths of R' Yosef's heart. He grew frightened: Who could it be who was screaming like this — and why? Perhaps a band of thieves had set upon a Jew. He rushed toward the source of the sound.

The shrill, deafening cries were coming from a house on the side of the road.

Inside, the scene was dreadful to behold: A dead man wrapped in a *tallis* lay on the floor, candles flickering all around him. Surrounding the corpse was a widow and her seven orphans wringing their hands, sobbing pitifully, and wailing, "Dear Father, why have you left us?" R' Yosef was touched by the chilling sight and joined in their weeping; the orphans cried even louder. From their words R' Yosef understood that their father had departed, leaving not even a solitary coin behind, and the bereaved family owned only the tattered shirts on their backs.

A short but difficult battle raged within his heart. There was enormous wealth awaiting him from the nobleman: He was all set to become the master of the village! A castle, a winter home, a summer residence. The village in its entirety, with its fields, orchards, vineyards, its rivers and the produce that grew by their banks. All this could be his —

And here, a widow whom he had never seen before, a family he did not know. Only one small step and he could be out of here. From far away, he would not hear their cries —

The battle took but a millisecond, a spark of eternity. He grasped the bag with both hands and handed it to the crying widow: "There are hundreds of rubles in this. You and your family can live off it for many years."

The widow turned bloodshot eyes towards him, unbelieving.

"Are my sufferings nothing, that you've come to pour salt in the wounds?" she asked. "What fool would believe that a complete stranger would give me such an enormous amount as a gift?"

But R' Yosef was adamant, as he handed her the sack of rubles. Another minute passed and he was gone, disappeared from view.

At that moment there was a great furor in Heaven. Had such a thing ever been heard of? A Jew had gone and sacrificed his entire fortune, every possession he owned, had given up the possibility of undreamed-of wealth and left himself penniless.

The Heavenly Court ruled that the Jew be given a priceless gift in exchange for his incredible deed. But Satan intervened, saying: "All *tzaddikim* are given tests before being granted gifts from Heaven. Let me go and test R' Yosef. If he stands up through the ordeal, he deserves the gift."

The one responsible for good tidings, Eliyahu *HaNavi* himself, intervened and said, "Satan will give him a test that no one can pass. If he must go through a trial before being granted the gift, I myself will go down and test him."

After having given all his money to the widow, R' Yosef tried to think what he should do next. He no longer had a home: he had sold it. He could not go to his landlord empty-handed. Now that he was left a pauper, bereft of every possession, he would travel from city to city, country to country, like all those itinerant wanderers, his hand outstretched. And who knew? Perhaps Heaven would have mercy on him and he would succeed.

But no: R' Yosef decided that he would not beg from any man, not for bread or a place to sleep. No, only if someone reached out and invited him would he agree to accept help.

One night he sat in a *shul*, in the dim light of a small candle that cut the darkness just a little. A short moment passed and it was extinguished, and the *shul* lay in complete and total blackness. R' Yosef sat, thinking about his situation. He was faint with hunger, thirsty and tired. Suddenly a terrible feeling arose in him, an emotion that had languished, unknown and unheeded, awaiting the right moment, a feeling clothed in the most destructive of garments: resentment and complaint.

"You fool, you gave all your money to a widow whom you'd never met, a stranger. And wouldn't any other Jew have helped her? She wouldn't have died of hunger, that's for certain! All that wealth in your hands — How happy Heaven must have been for this "mitzvah" of yours. After *Maariv* all the congregants simply disappeared, ignoring you as if you were nothing but air. So where is the justice? You gave everything you had, and you can't even find someone to give you hospitality for one night."

But R' Yosef struggled with all his strength to banish the drop of bitterness from his heart, and he ignored this evil feeling and its litany of complaint. "Get away from me!" he thought. "Do you think I will regret this good deed, you fool? Thank G-d for having sent such a mitzvah to me," he thought in satisfaction. "Whatever happens to me, I will not regret it and will hold onto it with all my might."

The squeaking of hinges announced the opening of the *shul* door. An old man with a handsome countenance walked in, wrapped in a thick winter coat. He sat down next to R' Yosef and lit a small candle.

"Hello, Reb Yid," the old man said, his face aglow. "I think you're not from this city. I don't recognize your face."

They exchanged some small talk. Somehow, the topic turned to the man's encounter with the widow. The old man pursed his lips and said, his surprise evident, "It's unbelievable. Can a man give everything he owns to someone he doesn't even know? And you've been left without anything at all?"

R' Yosef nodded his head in assent.

"G-d has been good to me and given me everything," the old man said. "He has blessed me with great wealth. I want to give you a nice sum that you can support yourself with, you and your family, for all your lives. You will even be able to open your own business, and if you succeed you will be rich. Just sell me your great mitzvah."

A mighty storm roared within R' Yosef at that moment, much like the one that had raged in the widow's house. He could be freed from his terrible poverty in a moment, make a respectable living, perhaps even go into business —

He steeled himself and said, "Absolutely not! After G-d gave me the merit of such a sacrifice, I won't sell it, not even if you give me the entire world!"

"And what about half the deed?" the old man asked. "Would you sell me half the deed? I will still give you the entire sum I had promised."

But R' Yosef hung onto the mitzvah and refused to sell even half of it. The old man persisted, asked for one third and one quarter of the mitzvah. He persisted until he offered him a goodly sum for just one percent of the deed!

"Not even for one thousandth," R' Yosef shouted. "I don't want money in exchange for a mitzvah!"

At that moment the old man revealed himself, and lo! it was Eliyahu *HaNavi* himself. The bearer of good news turned to R' Yosef: "You have passed your test! Now you can choose one of three gifts: a long life for you and your wife, or vast wealth, or a son who will be holy and who will bring great light with his piety and Torah learning."

"The money isn't worth anything to me, I can do without it," R' Yosef answered. "Long life? Even if I live for a thousand years, that's nothing compared with news of a son. I choose a son who will be a great *tzaddik*!"

And R' Yosef and his wife would not change their minds, even when Eliyahu told them that they would be destined to wander in poverty all their years.

After a short time they had a son whom they named Menachem — for he would bring them comfort. And he grew up to become the holy rebbe R' Menachem Mendel of Riminov, who indeed illuminated the world with his learning and awesome holiness. And his father, too, the innkeeper R' Yosef, merited to have his own name mentioned year after year, on the *yahrtzeit* of his son on the 19th day of Iyar. For R' Menachem Mendel had promised that good things would befall those who would mark his *yahrtzeit* by lighting a candle in honor of the soul of R' Menachem Mendel, son of R' Yosef.

The Abandoned Wife

"IN SANZ, THEY HIDE THEIR MIRACLES UNDER THE TABLE." Thus declared Rabbi Shmuel Engel, one of the greatest of the *chassidim* of Rabbi Chaim of Sanz, who spent many years in the company of his rebbe. The *Divrei Chaim* was once told by the *chassidim* of R' Tzvi Hirsch of Riminov that their rebbe would immerse himself in the ice cold waters of the *mikveh*, and that when the rebbe would emerge the waters would be hot. In response, R' Chaim replied tartly: "Among you *chassidim* everything is a big deal, everything is a miracle, and even warming up a *mikveh* is something special."

The *Divrei Chaim* himself worked mightily to conceal any miracles, camouflaging them in the guise of natural phenomena. Once, however, when there was a need to bring an "enlightened" Jew back to repentance, the Rebbe of Sanz ceased to hide his great powers. He knew that when the "enlightened" one would return to his house, he would spread the tale of the miracles he saw the Rebbe perform, and thus G-d's Name would be sanctified.

The *Divrei Chaim* would not relinquish that accomplishment, even at the expense of leaving the bounds of modesty that he had erected around himself!

That winter the cold had attacked Poland violently, even by the standards of that frigid country. Winter came earlier than usual that year, and a thin white layer already covered the earth on Yom Kippur. By the time Succos arrived, there was so much snow that it was impossible to sit in the *succah* on the first night of the holiday for more than the time it takes to quickly eat a *kezayis*. Even the oldest inhabitants declared that they could not remember such a harsh and bitter winter.

"And just now, when even the dogs are looking for a shelter

from the cold, you've decided to go to work?" Genendel asked her husband, Wolf, bitterly, as he put on his heavy winter coat.

Wolf just murmured a few words from beneath his thick mustache, as he threw more and more of his personal possessions into a sack.

"Don't I deserve an answer?" Genendel muttered angrily, leaving the room in tears. Her heart prophesied no good from this strange journey that had appeared from out of nowhere.

Two days before she had found a letter secreted in her husband's drawer. From its contents she realized that her husband, Wolf, was planning a long journey in the dead of winter. When she questioned her husband, his face had reddened with shame and anger and he had flung harsh words at her. Finally he announced that he had to sacrifice himself for the sake of making a living.

From that moment worry and fear crawled through her heart like insidious worms; she couldn't find a moment's peace, neither day nor night. She begged her husband not to leave her, and if not for her sake then for his — let him have mercy on his health. To no avail: Her words were a wasted effort. Wolf did not answer her at all.

Tears drifted down her face as she stood by the window watching the sleigh that flew swiftly away from the home, leaving behind it a broken heart and dismal memories. Peace was a rare commodity in this hut, a dream that had never been fulfilled.

Her worst fears were realized; all Genendel's suspicions came to pass. From the beginning she understood, through some keen intuition, that the story of a business trip was nothing more than that: a story.

Many months passed from the time of Wolf's departure; the terrible winter had ended and the wild flowers, in a blaze of color, were bringing joy to the hearts of all the people — except the bitter heart of Genendel. From the day Wolf had left home she had lost all trace of him. She waited hopefully for a letter, a sign that he had not completely cut his ties to her. She waited in vain.

Miserably she turned to the police to ask them to help her find her lost husband. The commander of the local station heard the details with stony politeness. At first, thinking the man was lost, he tried to help, but when he realized from her words that this was a case of desertion he closed the file immediately. "Foolish Jewess," he said with a chuckle, the mirth clear in his voice, "go find your husband yourself. The Polish police are too busy to take care of the marital problems of two Jews."

Genendel did all she could to track down her missing husband. She searched far and wide, sent letters and telegrams to all who knew him, to all his family members. She checked all the places where he had stayed in the past, spoke with all his business acquaintances.

And she came up with nothing. Wolf had vanished like a stone in the sea.

"I don't even ask that he return home anymore," she poured out her bitterness to one of her neighbors. "Just let him grant me a divorce, so that I'm not left an *agunah* all my life."

That neighbor's husband was a *chassid* of the Rebbe of Sanz. She told Genendel of the Rebbe's greatness and holiness, and how thousands of people had been helped by him.

"If you listen to me you'll travel to Sanz, and you'll be saved," she said fervently.

Genendel accepted her words with complete faith and she left for Sanz.

As she stood before the *Divrei Chaim,* she felt herself grow faint. These difficult months, and then the rigors and fatigue of the long journey from her hometown to Sanz, had left her drained. She burst into tears, her voice carrying through the entire house, melting the hearts of all who heard her. In a broken voice she told the Rebbe her woeful tale.

Rabbi Chaim sat at his desk. He dipped his pen into the inkwell and swiftly wrote a few lines. Then he placed two envelopes into her hand and said, "Go to Lemberg, the great city, and from there you will find the way to a certain village nearby. Give this letter to the Jew whose name I have written on the envelope."

Genendel failed to understand the significance of the second envelope nor did she see how an unimportant village near Lemberg would help her, but she had strong faith. Without questions or delay she quickly placed the envelopes into her pocket and set out on her way.

The train had traveled less than one third of the journey to Lemberg when the mystery of the second envelope was solved. She finally had a chance to look at it — and found her own name written upon it. She peeked inside. There, she found a large sum of money. "The holy Rebbe didn't want to shame me, so he found this roundabout way to support me," she thought, deeply moved. The first ray of hope and joy shone before her.

"The rabbi from Sanz is turning to me? What do I have to do with him? It cannot be." The envelope shook in the hands of Siegmund Schultz, a Jew of German extraction. He glared at her. "Have you come to make fun of me?" he screamed.

Genendel stood, thunderstruck. In her imagination she had envisioned the figure of an elderly, bearded *chassid* to whom the Rebbe had sent her for assistance. But to this German with his bare head? She would never have thought of such a thing!

"I haven't journeyed all the way from Sanz to laugh at you," she said earnestly.

"I've never even heard of the Rebbe of Sanz," the man muttered. "What does he want?"

He read through the letter while keeping up a ceaseless litany of complaint. Finally, he gave her a strange look.

"One of the two: Either you are crazy, or I am."

The *agunah* stood before him in all her misery. She, too, did not understand the meaning of this, but she was adamant in her belief that if the rebbe had sent her here there was a reason.

Siegmund read the letter a second time. Suddenly he laughed uproariously. He left Genendel, wholly confused, standing in his house while he raced out to the street, waving the paper in his hand.

"My friends, listen to this," he gathered together a group of the "enlightened." "What do you think of this?" In ceremonious tones he read them the contents of the letter. "Rabbi Halberstam writes to me to find the husband of some lady named Genendel from Poland. I'm the only one who can do it, he says!"

The crowd of scoffers broke out into laughter while Siegmund gleefully read the letter aloud again and again.

Genendel stood, watching the scene sadly. But she did not leave. Slowly, it dawned on Siegmund that this woman from Poland meant honestly and truly to stay in his house until he had found her husband for her.

"You are a foolish woman. Don't you understand that the *rabbiner* wanted to be rid of you, so he sent you to a distant place?" The joke was not over yet. "If you want to stay here in my house, you can take the place of the maid, who left us recently."

And so Genendel took the place of the maidservant. All that week she toiled. Her master occasionally remembered to ask her if she had heard something of her missing husband, whose desire to be rid of her was becoming clear to him.

A week passed. There were times when she felt she would explode. On Shabbos Siegmund tried to have her do things which would desecrate the day, but one look from her told him he had overstepped his bounds.

On Sunday the German called to her.

"I'm planning to travel to Lemberg and my shoes need to be fixed. Take them and give them to the cobbler who lives in this building."

Genendel obediently left, the shoes in her hands. She knocked on the cobbler's door.

"Mr. Siegmund asked that you repair these —"

And then she screamed, her eyes widening. For the cobbler sitting before her, tiny nails in his mouth and a hammer in his hand, looked astonishingly like Wolf, her missing husband.

The cobbler, too, gave out a surprised yell. He tried to stand up and run but Genendel's shouting seemed to rivet him to his chair.

All the building's tenants, among them Siegmund Schultz, were witnesses to the public display. Despite his efforts, the cobbler could not deny the connection between them.

Genendel left the Lemberg *beis din* a victor, the divorce papers in her hand.

"It is a wondrous thing," whispered Siegmund, a *yarmulke* resting a bit uneasily upon his head. "Perhaps I should travel to Sanz."

The Sign of the Twins

YITZCHAK, SON OF R' SHLOMO, THE RABBI OF VIENNA, was a marvelously talented lad, handsome and brilliant in Torah learning. People who saw him almost inevitably wished on themselves a son such as he. And the city's *shadchanim* were soon banging on R' Shlomo's door, offering incomparable matches. But R' Shlomo put them off day after day, month after month. "Wait a little longer," he would tell the matchmakers. "My son, Yitzchak, is still young. He wants only to learn now, not to carry the responsibility of a family."

Gimpel the matchmaker wouldn't accept such excuses. "Rabbi, am I offering him slavery? I'll make him a master!"

Gimpel was suggesting a match with Mindeh, the lovely daughter of R' Shimshon Hektzin, one of Vienna's wealthiest and most respected citizens. R' Shimshon was determined to win the gifted son of the city's rav, and every month raised the amount he was offering as a dowry for his daughter.

Now Gimpel arrived at the rabbi's home, in his pocket an offer that the rabbi undoubtedly could not refuse. "The bride brings with her a dowry that is unsurpassed: the estate that belonged to Prince Siegmund that R' Shimshon has bought. It stands in the midst of the forest, a beautiful building surrounded on all sides by pools and gardens. Your brilliant son can sit and learn undisturbed there. Servants will do all the work in his great house; his wife will be dedicated to only one thing: her husband's Torah study. What's wrong with that?"

"There is nothing wrong," R' Shlomo said, shocked by the generous offer. "Let me think about it carefully."

But because R' Shlomo did not get back to him quickly, Hektzin assumed he was not interested, and he married his daughter off to another talented young man from Amsterdam.

Not long afterwards, Yitzchak turned 18, and his father decided that soon he would carefully scrutinize the many offers that had been made, and choose the best from among them.

It was a springlike day; the sun generously displayed its rays after the snowy and frigid winter. Breathtaking flowers waved gaily in the city's gardens, and all the world seemed to sing.

The group of young men who had gathered in R' Shlomo's classroom in his house in the Jewish Quarter, though, were oblivious to nature's grand displays, for they were concentrating on a deep Talmudic concept. The Rav gave a complex lesson, and they listened carefully. The smartest among them even managed to argue volubly with their teacher.

The Rav's son, Yitzchak, strongly defended the position of his father, the *rosh yeshivah*, debating with one of the brightest students. The sound of discourse grew louder.

In the heat of the argument Yitzchak grew very excited. He stood up and paced around the room, deep in thought. The walls of the classroom seemed to close in on him. Almost of their own volition his legs took him out to the large garden that bordered the palace.

Among the thick foliage Yitzchak found a haven for his agitated feelings. The fresh air cooled his burning cheeks like a soothing ripple of water. Here he could concentrate and delve even deeper into the complexities of the matter. He leaned his head, covered with the sweat of hard work, on one of the tree branches and sank into thought.

From one of the benches in the park, a pair of dark eyes gazed at him. Princess Wilhelmina, the king's only daughter, had gone for a stroll in the pleasant air, and was struck by the image of the young Jewish lad walking back and forth, his eyes half-closed in deep concentration and his brow furrowed in thought.

She had never before seen such a sight. Gentile young men of his age, if they were rich, spent their time playing cards and dice and other such gentlemanly pursuits. And if poor, they struggled for a piece of bread, their faces blackened with toil. But such a handsome lad, whose face testified that he was well bred and of the wealthy classes, to be pacing back and forth like this? What was bothering him? What was he thinking of?

She tried to call out to him and engage him in conversation, but the handsome young man did not hear her.

The princess stared at him for some time. She began to understand that this was no personal problem that was troubling him, but rather a purely spiritual matter. A grim determination began to grow within her: Why should she seek her fortune among the frivolous youths who spent their entire lives in pursuit of trivial and foolish pleasures? How much more fortunate she would be if she found a husband who possessed such deep spiritual power!

She followed the young man until she saw his slender figure disappear behind the gates of the Jewish ghetto. She called to her servants and ordered them to follow him until they found out who he was.

After a few days the servants appeared before her. Mission accomplished: They revealed that the young man was none other than the son of the city's rabbi.

The young woman then went to her father, the king. "I want to marry Yitzchak, son of the rabbi."

The king shuddered. Surely his lovely daughter must be joking! But the young woman repeated her request again and again, until her father called out in fury, "You rebellious girl, has the devil entered you? Princes whose lineage can be traced through 20 generations of royalty are begging for your hand and you're dreaming about marrying a Jew?"

"Yes."

The king pushed her away; his refusal was absolute. And the girl, who grew up pampered and indulged and had never before been confronted with the word "no," grew seriously ill.

Her parents, the king and queen, spoke endlessly to her, begging her, entreating, but she would not listen. They could not understand why their daughter had chosen to humiliate them so dreadfully. Instead of marrying a prince or nobleman, she had chosen a miserable Jew!

The girl, out of her desire to marry only Yitzchak, built a wall around her heart. Her illness grew worse, and the threat of death hung over her.

When her father, the king, saw that the life of his only daughter was in danger, he grudgingly surrendered and agreed to invite the Jewish boy to his palace and offer him her hand in marriage.

A friendship of many years existed between R' Shlomo and Dietrich of Zisheim, His Majesty's Finance Minister. That day the king confided his troubles to Dietrich.

With day's end, a slow-moving, dark figure sneaked into the ghetto. Dietrich's servant reached the rabbi's house, and knocked quietly on the heavy door.

"My master commanded me to give this to the rabbi," he whispered to the rebbetzin, handing her a scroll tied with a heavy linen thread.

R' Shlomo read through the strange missive:

"My dear friend, the king has told me today that his daughter, Princess Wilhelmina, refuses to marry any man other than your son, Yitzchak. Very soon a servant will call upon you and command you to bring your son to him."

"Woe is me!" R' Shlomo wept brokenly, the rolled-up letter falling to the ground from his shaking hands. "Woe is me for my sins!"

Shocked, the rebbetzin raced to him. She bent down and quickly read the letter. When she finished reading the Finance Minister's words her knees buckled and she almost fell down in a faint.

For a long while the parents wrung their hands and wept bitter tears. This was the king's decree: Who dared to refuse? But could it be that their son would marry a gentile woman?

At the sound of their cries, several neighbors and friends came running. Hearing the news, they traded ideas and advice. Finally Tuvia, head of the community, said, "The princess wants your unmarried son. But she would not want him if she knew he was married —"

"What are you saying?" The rabbi's eyes lit up.

"I'm saying," Tuvia said, laughing, "that you'd better hurry up and get Yitzchak married, and you can't do it soon enough!"

Relief coursed through the rabbi's home. The terrible anxiety was gone. And yet, when they began looking for an appropriate girl, they discovered that it was impossible to arrange such a swift match. All the respectable possibilities seemed to have disappeared.

With growing concern, the rabbi and rebbetzin searched everywhere, and came up with nothing. That is, until the rebbetzin noticed Bluma, the young girl who worked in their home. She cried out joyously, "I've found someone fine. Bluma will marry our son!"

Bluma the maid, with no particular claim to beauty, no eminent lineage, no money, and no parents, possessed only one important trait: She was an unmarried Jewish girl!

R' Shlomo called together 10 men, wrote a *kesubah* and put up a *chupah*. The rebbetzin pulled out a little cake and some pastries left over from Shabbos, and a few jugs of wine from the basement. And so the brilliant Yitzchak was married. In their worst nightmares the rabbi and rebbetzin had never dreamed that their splendid son would marry a simple and homely maidservant in a swift and somber ceremony, with hardly an invited guest to celebrate the event.

In a few days R' Shlomo saw the wisdom of Tuvia's advice. A royal carriage raced through the ghetto streets and stopped beneath his window. Two uniformed soldiers knocked loudly on his door and showed him the king's command.

R' Shlomo read the royal proclamation. His heart thudded. "Thank Heaven for having granted me a miracle in this place," he murmured to himself.

In his letter, the king commanded R' Shlomo to send him his son, in order to teach him the rudiments of Christianity as preparation for his marriage to Princess Wilhelmina.

A hint of laughter gleamed in his eyes. "What does the king want of my son?" he asked in obvious wonder. "He is a married man!"

The messengers were stumped. They suspected they were being fooled, but the rabbi immediately called in his son and daughter-in-law, who testified that they were bound in marriage. Perturbed, the soldiers returned to the palace. Later, an even more impressive entourage arrived, and it too was informed of the tie that bound the handsome and charming young man, Yitzchak, with the dumpy young woman who dared to call herself his wife.

And the decree was annulled!

The rabbi and rebbetzin waited several weeks and when it was clear that the danger was over, the rebbetzin summoned her maid and began to hint to her that it would be appropriate for her to give back the unexpected gift that had fallen into her hands. The maid turned a naive and questioning face to her. The rebbetzin, eventually eschewing subtlety, told her in language easily understood that she ought to accept a divorce, for the marriage, after all, had been simply an emergency arrangement.

"Absolutely not," Bluma answered. "My marriage was a proper one and I will not give it up."

The rebbetzin called her son and commanded him to give his wife a divorce, as she was not his proper partner. But Yitzchak would not hear of it. "This was destined in heaven," he said. "G-d checked all the matches, examined all the factors, and caused this to happen, because in the natural way there would have been no chance of the rabbi's son marrying the maidservant Bluma."

His mother stared at him and said, in broken tones, "Yitzchak, my son, are you mad? The greatest in the land are nothing compared to you, and you will stay tied to a homely maid?"

"Yes," Yitzchak answered. "I prefer to be tied to the maidservant, who is beautiful in my eyes, rather than to humiliate a Jewish woman."

It is said: At that moment a great furor broke out in heaven, and the Heavenly Tribunal judged that Yitzchak should be granted a great gift. Bluma, that good wife, bore Yitzchak 24 children, all beautiful as roses, sensitive and successful — 12 pairs of twins. And from these twins came the famed Teomim (twins) family, now spread through the entire earth.

A Gift for the Bride

CONGRATULATIONS! THE ENGAGEMENT WAS ANNOUNCED. The young groom was R' Dovid Tzvi Shlomo, a youth of 15, still beardless, son of R' Elazar Mendel, who emigrated to the Holy Land from Lelov, Poland. The *chasan's* father lived in a small, neglected apartment, almost a ruin, in one of the dark alleys of Jerusalem's Old City.

The bride, Miriam, also very young, was the daughter of the *tzaddik,* R' Pinchas HaLevi Horowitz, known to all as Reb Pinchas Bruder for his Galician hometown of Brod, where he lived before his arrival in *Eretz Yisrael.* R' Pinchas could boast of great lineage, as grandson of the holy brothers R' Shmelke of Nikolsburg and R' Pinchas of Frankfurt-am-Main, author of the *Haflaah.*

The matchmaker had worked assiduously to bring the two sides together. There was a great distance between them: R' Elazar Mendel had chosen to live in Jerusalem, while R' Pinchas of Brud had made the holy city of Tzefas his home. For this reason, the match had taken considerable time to complete. R' Elazar Mendel and his wife, Rebbetzin Faiga Mattil, had traveled with their young son Duvid'l to distant Tzefas. From the Jaffa Gate they had left Jerusalem in a donkey-drawn wagon, and they covered over half the distance within it. When they reached the outskirts of the Galil, they completed the journey on the backs of mules.

The young bridegroom, Duvid'l, was a charming lad. His curly blonde *peyos,* reaching to his chest, swung gently; a fire seemed to burn in his eyes and piercing glance. A few years before this, in 5610 (1850), his grandfather, R' Moshe of Lelov, had left his Diaspora home to live in *Eretz Yisrael.* Before his departure he had traveled around to take leave of the great men of his generation. On his way he had detoured to Sadegora to ask for a blessing from R' Yisrael of Ruzhin. R' Yisrael had taken the sweet little 6-year-old, Duvid'l, on his knee, played with him, then stared for some time into his beautiful eyes, crying at the same time, "Such holy eyes, such brilliant eyes!"

The court at Sadegora was left in a ferment: When had the Rebbe ever taken a child onto his lap and played with him? The Ruzhiners explained the phenomenon: "This child, this darling youngster, will never sin! Eyes such as these will never look upon anything sinful!"

After the engagement, R' Pinchas was traveling from Tzefas to Yerushalayim, accompanied by his thoughts of satisfaction and contentment. He recognized that his daughter's fiancée was a gem, a treasure that would retain its worth eternally. Despite the young boy's humility one could sense that he was a lofty soul, vibrant with G-d's spirit within.

The green hills of the Upper Galil began to give way to the brown hues of the valley. The sparkling blue of the Kineret grew smaller and smaller as he traveled farther. The carriage made its way over the sandy, stony road. Orchards gave off a heady aroma of fruit. R' Pinchas hardly noticed the path before him. He had the reputation of one who could be so immersed in his learning that the entire physical realm seemed to disappear. After all, hadn't the Sages referred negatively to a person who interrupted his learning to say, "What a beautiful tree…"? He hastily pulled a Gemara out from the folds of his coat and began to learn.

R' Pinchas never slept on Shabbos, from the beginning of the holy day to its end. From the time the Friday night meal was finished, he would pore over his beloved books, studying the weekly *parashah* and all its commentaries, and then moving on to Gemara and *Tosafos*. His library included books of Kabbalah and the *Zohar*, and he would spend hours delving into hidden wisdom as well.

He would bend over his holy books by the light of a flickering candle, his sweet humming filling the house. Not far away, the kettle sitting on the stove gave its muted whistle; the snuffbox sat ready on the table. During the night he would occasionally pour himself a cup of boiling black coffee. In his other hand, between thumb and forefinger, he would take a pinch of aromatic snuff. Between breaths he would sip the hot liquid, and feel energized once again. All this without ever taking his eyes off whichever book was open in front of him.

People in the know in Tzefas would say that in the course of the night R' Pinchas would drink 24 cups of coffee and use up an entire box of tobacco.

Every Friday R' Pinchas would visit the spice shop. The salesman knew him well. Without a word he would take a large spoonful of coffee beans from a wooden container covered with the stamps of Brazil's customs and excise authorities. He would bring these beans to a small grinder, and carefully pour the ground coffee into a cone-shaped brown bag. Then he would take another generous spoonful, this time of freshly ground tobacco, and fill another bag. *Ahh*, the smell of the tobacco and the coffee — it filled the entire shop, every corner. R' Pinchas would leave the store, two bags in hand, each giving off a marvelous aroma. This was R' Pinchas's custom, every Friday.

When R' Pinchas grew old, he no longer had the strength to visit the spice shop himself. Then his beloved son-in-law, R' Duvid'l, who lived in Tzefas for a long time after his marriage, would purchase the tobacco and the coffee for him.

"Once," R' Duvid'l told the story, laughing, "I was in a hurry because of Shabbos, and I mixed up the bags of tobacco and coffee. I put the coffee into the snuffbox, and the tobacco into the kettle. They were the same dark color, so I didn't notice my mistake."

His father-in-law, R' Pinchas, didn't notice either. He sat and learned all that night, drank 24 cups of tobacco without a murmur. Only after Shabbos did he ask, "What's happened this week? Why does the tobacco have such a strange odor?"

"I smelled the 'tobacco,' " R' Duvid'l ended, "and immediately raced to the kettle. From inside came the wonderful smell of tobacco."

The sound of the horses' hooves ceased.

"We'll stop here," the wagoner announced. "The horses will be fed, and the gentleman can *daven Minchah*."

After prayers R' Pinchas began to think about his wife's parting words to him. "Why haven't the in-laws sent the traditional gifts to our daughter, Miriam?" His brow wrinkled with the effort of concentration.

His *mechutan* — His brain whirled, as he pictured the miserable hovel that housed his daughter's future in-laws in Jerusalem. The *mechutan* was, after all, a penniless pauper. There was a reason the in-laws had not yet sent the customary gifts to their prospective daughter-in-law. The *mechutan* spent all his days in his tiny room deep in learning and G-d's service, and he did not pay attention to his family's physical sustenance. Once, when hunger had descended even more bitterly than usual on the house, the rebbetzin, Faige Mattil, had knocked on her husband's door with a request: "We can't go on any longer; we'll all die of hunger, Heaven forbid."

R' Elazar Mendel's heart had melted before the plea of his pious wife, a granddaughter of the *Chozeh* of Lublin. He left his room and stood deep in thought for some minutes. Then he roused himself from his reverie. "Enough, I've wasted two full minutes from my service of G-d," he said, before returning to his room.

R' Pinchas knew of this, and thus his wife's parting words disturbed him greatly:

"When you get to Jerusalem, to our *mechutan*, don't forget to remind him that the bride has not received the customary gifts."

"*Nu?*" R' Pinchas's wife and daughter, the bride, surrounded him upon his return from Jerusalem. R' Pinchas opened wide his empty hands in a gesture of despair.

"Why haven't you brought back a gift for the bride?" his wife repeated, her tone of voice bitter.

R' Pinchas shrugged his shoulders. Go and tell your wife that from the moment you entered the *mechutan's* home you sensed his spirit surging up to heaven, flitting about in the higher spheres. The *mechutan* gave off the taste of *Gan Eden*; small wonder, then, that all the foolishness of this world was forgotten in his presence. At a moment like that could you possibly remember to ask for a piece of jewelry for a bride?

The days of the engagement passed, the months flew by. The bride's mother found herself expecting less and less that the in-laws in Jerusalem would remember to send her daughter a gift.

"How can you keep quiet about it?" she fretted to her husband, as she packed his belongings for another trip to Jerusalem. "Doesn't your daughter's humiliation bother you at all?"

R' Pinchas all but vowed that this time he would not forget, and yet, the moment he entered the bare home of R' Elazar Mendel in Jerusalem, and once again breathed its rarefied air, the entire matter of a golden pin for the bride seemed childish and silly. Of course, there were times when the words hovered upon his lips. But each time he would look around at the small, bare home, whose incredible poverty seemed to scream out from every corner. He would see the children sipping thin soup, nothing more than water boiled up with bran. Feeling deeply shamed, he simply could not bring up the subject.

About the bran soup, too, he heard a story. A few years before, when his future son-in-law Duvid'l was still a young boy and the house was already trapped in the unrelenting jaws of deprivation, Duvid'l and his sister, Devorah Golda, had been sitting down to eat some bran soup. Devorah Golda insisted that her brother Duvid'l should get the larger portion, since he was learning Torah in *cheder* and he needed the energy for his studies. Duvid'l, though, retorted: "No, my dear sister, you should get more, because you stay at home with Mommy all day and have to help her."

Two hungry children —

While they were arguing, a beggar walked in, drank up all the soup in one gulp, and ended all discussion.

And R' Pinchas heard still more about the hunger in the house. Once, R' Elazar Mendel could not bear his children's starvation, and he left his room to prepare them food. A pot containing thin gruel stood on the coals, and R' Elazar Mendel fanned the flames with his hat. Not used to doing so, he failed to get the fire going well. His daughter Devorah Golda called out, "Father, go faster, I'm dying of hunger!" When her father heard her words, and realized just how far things had gone, two tears of anguish fell from his eyes.

Years later, as an old woman, Devorah Golda would add, when telling the story, "All my life I haven't stopped repenting for this deed, for having brought sorrow to my father!"

If R' Pinchas wanted to find out what he could expect from his prospective in-laws, now he knew.

Before the wedding the entire family journeyed from Tzefas to Yerushalayim. They arrived at the gates of the city a few days before Shavuos. The gifts, needless to say, had not arrived. The rebbetzin Faiga Mattil went out to greet the bride, her hands empty. The bride's mother felt her heart would break. At the inn she poured out her heart to her husband.

"The entire time I consoled myself that the *mechutanim* wouldn't humiliate the bride before her wedding. And now I'm completely disappointed. Couldn't they even get her an '*aybel*,' worth almost nothing?"

This '*aybel*' was a modest piece of jewelry, a small golden coin hung on a simple chain that was worn around the neck. In those days when bread was rare and water scarce, even this was not easy to come by.

R' Pinchas hung his head in confusion; he had nothing to say.

Two days before the Shavuos holiday, a long procession wended its way through the narrow alleys, toward Mt. Zion. It was an ancient Yerushalmi custom to visit the grave of King David before Shavuos, the anniversary of his death. R' Elazar Mendel walked among the large group. A few steps behind him stood his *mechutan*, R' Pinchas.

The crowd was enveloped in a spiritual aura.

And like a thief, the brazen thought stole into R' Pinchas's mind: "And why, after all, shouldn't they give the bride an *'aybel'*?"

The thought had hardly been formulated when R' Elazar Mendel, the *mechutan*, turned to R' Pinchas and said, in tones of wonder, "*Mechutan*, we're walking to our holy King David, two days before the giving of the Torah, and you're thinking about an *'aybel'*?"

R' Pinchas returned to his inn after prayers, completely dumbfounded. He turned to his wife.

"Please don't get me involved in these matters anymore. It's enough that we have a *mechutan* who has *ruach hakodesh*, a man of the heavens. Do you really need silly gifts too?"

Entrance Ticket to Gan Eden

THE CITY OF UMAN WAS ABUZZ WITH NEWS. "HAVE YOU heard?" one Jew asked the other. "R' Naftali the Elder has returned!"

"How can it be?" others wondered. "Didn't he travel to *Eretz Yisrael* to die there and be buried in its holy earth? Why has he come back?"

No one knew the answer. R' Naftali, a wine merchant, had been among the city's most prominent citizens. All his life he'd run his business by the dictates of the Sages: Make your Torah permanent and your labor temporary. Had he sold enough bottles of wine to bring in food sufficient for the day? If so, he would leave the barrels of wine, sit in the *beis midrash*, and immediately begin to hum the sing-song melody of Gemara learning.

R' Naftali merited a two-fold blessing: His Torah learning was excellent and his business prosperous. His family members enjoyed a respectable living and yet he was accepted among the rabbis and the *chassidim* of the city as a man learned in Torah and G-d's service. His years passed in serenity and satisfaction; he watched his business grow and he saw all his children and grandchildren involved in Torah learning.

When R' Naftali grew old he began thinking about moving to *Eretz Yisrael*, to spend the last years of his life on its earth and, when his time came, to be interred within its rocky soil. R' Naftali gave his business over to his children, commanded them to take care of his household and willed all his possessions to them during his lifetime. And with that he was ready to leave for *Eretz Yisrael* with a sack full of money.

All his friends and admirers took leave of him; many wept. They heaped blessings upon him, wished that he would merit to hear the shofar of the *Mashiach* before his time came, prayed that he would witness the dead coming back to rejoice in their resurrection. Thus did they say goodbye, and when his carriage had disappeared from view they continued to murmur blessings, all feeling a strong yearning for the friend who had left them for the earth of another land.

But now the strange news was heard: R' Naftali has returned.

His friends surrounded him, begging him to reveal the reason for his return after so much effort had been put into preparing for the journey. But R' Naftali was silent. He didn't give so much as a hint of why he changed his mind. Tired from his journey back and forth, he left the crowd that had gathered, and returned to his home. And the matter remained a mystery among the people of Uman.

After a short time R' Naftali contracted the illness that was to bring on his death. He commanded his sons to bring the *chevrah kaddisha* to his side. His sons, understanding that their father was about to return his soul to his Creator, burst out in bitter tears and called the men.

The *gabbaim* of the *chevrah kaddisha* entered the home. The head of the group prepared the candles to be lit in honor of the soul's passing.

When R' Naftali saw the *chevrah kaddisha*, the shadow of a smile appeared on his face. He began to chat with them of this and that, speaking of past events, not at all like a man standing at the edge of the abyss. Not only that, but R' Naftali's countenance did not resemble that of a man standing beneath the shadow of the Angel of Death.

After an hour or two had passed, the *chevrah kaddisha* realized that R' Naftali had made a mistake. They left, unwilling to waste their time any further.

The next day R' Naftali's sons appeared before the *chevrah kaddisha* again and asked that they come to their father. "What does he look like?" they asked. "Like yesterday." The members of the *chevrah kaddisha* responded testily, "Are you here to drive us crazy? If your father is destined to live, you should be dancing in the streets! Don't call us until you see he's almost dead."

"But we don't know what the signs of death are," the sons protested weakly.

The *gabbaim* pondered the matter. The man was critically ill, and he had called for them. True, he had called them for nothing yesterday. But that was yesterday. Today? His sickness must have gotten worse.

They took their equipment in hand and brought 10 men to the sick man's house. R' Naftali saw them and immediately began a conversation with them that had nothing to do with his imminent death.

The *gabbaim* of the *chevrah kaddisha* were now growing angry. Twice already the man had wasted their time. They stomped out of the house.

On the third day, the sons again approached the *chevrah kaddisha,* telling them that their father was about to return his soul to Heaven and that they must come immediately. The *gabbaim* did not want to hear about it; they sent the sons away. The sons told their father what had happened, and he implored them to calm the *gab-baim*. "Tell them that I know absolutely that my hour has come, and if they come I will reveal to them why I had them come twice for nothing."

The *chevrah kaddisha*, only half convinced, came to the sick man's house for a third time, prepared to do their dismal job.

When they entered the house they saw the difference immediately. The sick man's face had just one spark of life left in it; he was pale and breathing with difficulty. "Come closer," he whispered weakly.

The *gabbaim* approached the deathbed. The invalid began to speak. "I want to tell you something that happened to me many years ago."

Green fields surrounded R' Naftali as far as his eye could see on the road to Berditchev. Trees heavy with scarlet apples gave off an enchanting fragrance that tickled his nose and reminded him that spring was upon them.

In the days of his youth, before he became a wine merchant, R' Naftali had worked in the fabric trade. He would travel between different cities and their fairs, hawking his wares. Once in a while his travels would take him to the big city of Berditchev.

R' Naftali would never miss the opportunity to see the great *tzaddik* living there, and would actually detour from his route in order to visit the city and its rabbi.

On that trip he was returning from a fair and, as was his custom, he turned off towards Berditchev. He impatiently hurried the wagon driver, asking to be brought to the home of R' Levi Yitzchak. When the carriage finally stood before the house he jumped swiftly off, his purse in his hand. With long steps he approached the house and knocked.

One of the family members opened the door. "Hush," he whispered. "The *tzaddik* is just about to pray."

"That's not a problem," R' Naftali thought happily. "To hear R' Levi Yitzchak's prayers gives a man a taste of the next world."

The *tzaddik* was preparing to *daven*. He wrapped himself in his *tallis* and said the verses that precede prayer with awesome fervor. He had not yet put on his *tefillin* when the sound of men and women arguing began to resound from the courtyard outside. Pandemonium broke out, a wild melee of shouting voices. The *gabbai* walked out to quiet the people and they fell upon him with the urgent request for an immediate judgment by R' Levi Yitzchak, who, of course, served as the city's rabbi.

The litigants immediately entered. The *tzaddik* ceased praying and sat down. R' Naftali sat in an adjoining room and listened intently.

A man began: "I am a poor man, I make a bit of money for food by working as a moneychanger. But where do I get money from? I borrow a large sum from friends and change the money for those who need it. I charge a small fee, and thus I repay my loan.

"Yesterday 300 rubles that I had prepared to return to one of my friends was stolen from me. I have no means of sustenance left. How can I get 300 rubles together, and who will lend me more if word gets out that I borrow without returning? Who stole the money? Obviously, it must be the girl who comes in to clean the house. She must have seen me hide the money. Let her return it immediately!"

The maid claimed: "I never touched a cent that didn't belong to me, and I never even saw that money. This man has cursed and libeled me, and even picked up a stick and hit me as if I were a mad dog. I don't forgive him the insult."

The maid's parents claimed: "Let justice be done! Our daughter is innocent; she never touched that money and the man hit her for nothing. Can such a thing be?"

The Rabbi ruled: "Truth can be recognized. The maid didn't steal the money; let the moneychanger ask her forgiveness and compensate her for the blows. And yet, the truth of the moneychanger's words can also be seen: His money has been stolen. Someone else stole it. But where is the stolen money? I don't know."

At that moment R' Levi Yitzchak jumped up and paced back and forth. His face was troubled at his inability to help one of the litigants. Suddenly he stopped his frantic walking and stood still, his eyes focused on the ceiling. "Master of the Universe," he cried, "if only there were someone here who would give me 300 rubles to help pay back the moneychanger for his loss — such a person would earn his place in the World to Come in one short hour!"

In the adjoining room R' Naftali searched through his possessions. He had more than 300 rubles; dared he give them up? Money comes, money goes, but to be promised the World to Come? That did not happen often, certainly. Like a mighty wind, he flew into the next room and said, "My dear Rebbe, I will do your bidding. If I give the money, will you guarantee me, in writing, that I have a place in the World to Come?"

"Yes," the *tzaddik* said on the spot.

In the presence of the parents, the maid, and the moneychanger, R' Naftali handed the money to his rebbe, who gave it to the victim of the theft. Before their departure all the litigants heaped blessings on the Rabbi who brought such light to their lives. He did not let them leave until he had blessed the young girl to merit a good match for the baseless suspicion that had blackened her name. The moneychanger, too, he blessed, that he should never know any other loss.

When the Rabbi had finished his prayers, the merchant approached him hesitantly. "And what of my guarantee?"

Immediately, ink, a pen, and a piece of paper were brought before them. The Rabbi went to a corner and wrote something, folded the paper so that no one should see the words he penned, and said to R' Naftali: "Guard this note all your life, but never read it. When your time comes you will know it. At that time give the note to the men of the *chevrah kaddisha*, and they will bury it with you."

And R' Naftali did, indeed, keep the note all his life. He never looked to see what was written within it. He had a wonderful idea to keep it safe: He had a bookbinder bind it into the spine of his *siddur*.

"Now imagine," the dying man said to the *chevrah kaddisha,* "for 50 years I've guarded that *siddur.* And when I reached *Eretz Yisrael* I realized, to my horror, that of all things, in the confusion of packing I had forgotten the *siddur* — in Uman!

"At that moment my world grew dark; I felt exiled from a wonderful land. I realized that I had one of two choices: to be buried in the holy earth of *Eretz Yisrael,* but without R' Levi Yitzchak's note, or to be buried in the land of the gentiles together with the holy Rabbi's guarantee. I decided to return: *Eretz Yisrael* is *Eretz Yisrael,* but a guarantee of the World to Come?

"I took a place on board a ship returning to Europe. Now you can understand why I returned to Uman. I realized that it had been decreed upon me to be buried together with the note.

"When I grew ill and weak, I was sure my time had come, but when you arrived I had regained a little strength and I remembered the Rebbe's words: When your time comes you will know it yourself.

"No," I told myself, "I don't feel it yet." And so I turned the conversation to trivial matters. The same thing happened the next day. But now I know clearly that my last hour has come. I want to confess my sins and ask that the note be buried with me."

And when he finished speaking the dying man handed them a note. Soon thereafter, he passed away.

R' Naftali was escorted to the cemetery by a large group, and was buried with great respect. The *chevrah kaddisha,* particularly, seemed careful with the deceased's honor. Only they knew the secret of the note that went to the grave with him.

"R' Levi Yitzchak forbade only him to read the note," they told each other after R' Naftali's death, before they had prepared the body. "We are not included in the prohibition, certainly not now when the man is dead."

They opened the paper, their hearts pounding as they read the words. "Open the gates of *Gan Eden* to him. Levi Yitzchak, son of Sarah Sasha."

To End an Engagement, and to Forgive

EVEN BEFORE KASRIEL TURNED 18, THEY HAD BEGUN TO point him out. Dozens of matchmakers knocked on his father's door, bringing a myriad of suggestions: rich girls, girls whose fathers were rabbis, girls whose fathers were judges, *poskim*. Only the finest, most outstanding girls were recommended.

Not that Kasriel was such a remarkable young man. True, he was a good-tempered boy, who knew how to learn, *davened* properly, and showed reverence for G-d. But in Poland there were many such young men, and no one showered upon them so many possible matches.

But Kasriel was a golden lad, for he was the son of the wealthy R' Menashe, owner of five forests in Poland. Rumor had it that R' Menashe was one of the country's richest men, possibly the wealthiest of all.

No wonder, then, that the matchmakers wouldn't give R' Menashe a moment's peace. Each claimed that his suggestion was the best, and each looked forward eagerly to the generous matchmaking fee.

Finally, R' Menashe chose "Moshe Shadchan," of Cracow, who carried with him the most worthy match, the modest Mirel, daughter of the great wheat merchant Shalom Shachna of Cracow. Shalom Shachna's holdings approached those of R' Menashe, and the two wealthy men decided that this was the most appropriate possibility.

The date of the wedding was fixed for within one year of the engagement; the two sides would agree on a date. All of Jewish Poland waited with bated breath for this lavish wedding, which undoubtedly would be spoken of for years afterwards. "Money goes to money," men declared. "Would the millionaire forester even consider marrying his son off to the daughter of Muttel the cobbler?"

The news of the broken engagement hit Polish Jewry like a thunderbolt on a dark night. First the news was denied, but time passed without a sign of preparation for a wedding, lending credence to the dismal tidings of the broken match.

After some days had passed, the reasons for the engagement's end also became known. Shalom Shachna fled his house after going bankrupt and all his property was turned over to his creditors. Nothing was left of his legendary wealth; the bride could not even bring 100 zlotys as a dowry.

The match was broken. But the forester, R' Menashe, and his son, Kasriel, were not left alone for long. The matchmakers once again gathered, clamoring around his home like bees in a hive. Fortunate is one whose luck holds: As long as he has his wealth, he has his friends; he is never alone, and all want to be with him. Shalom Shachna's family felt the opposite effect: Except for a few creditors and the administrator of the poorhouse, no one paid them any attention at all.

Only a few weeks passed and Kasriel found himself engaged to the wonderful young girl, Breindel, daughter of the fiery genius R' Avigdor David Nathanson, a Torah leader in Kashimir. This time R' Menashe chose Torah learning and great lineage rather than wealth. The terrible lesson of the first match had left him shaken to the core. "Money can be lost, but Torah is an eternal possession. Whatever happens, R' Avigdor David will never turn into an ignoramus."

Three months later the wedding took place, with all the expected lavishness and pomp. The Jews of Poland spoke of its elegance, of the mounds of pastries and wonderful fare served to the thousands of guests. Even the meal served to the poor was unique; R' Menashe had instructed that no less than 500 poor men be invited to the meal that took place the night before the wedding, and an army of waiters stood by to serve them the best of foods.

Not a bone was left from the mountains of stuffed geese and roasted capons. The memory of the affair had faded with the passing of months. The bride and groom built their home in the capital city of Warsaw. Under the influence of his illustrious father-in-law, Kasriel spent many years immersed in Torah study, and only with R' Menashe's aging and increasing infirmity did he slowly begin to take part in the forestry business. Gradually, he took more and more responsibility away from his father, and after R' Menashe's death, Kasriel took his place. He was plunged into the business of forestry from morning to night, and his affairs took him all over the length and breadth of Poland.

Kasriel's wealth was huge, and he had enough to divide among 10 heirs. But 20 years had passed since his wedding and still he had no child. His huge house remained empty and lonely. His wife, Breindel, waited, heartbroken, for the merry sounds of children playing — but there were none. Kasriel, busy as he was all day with his business, felt the hurt of solitude less than his wife, but Breindel would not leave him be: Whenever his travels took him to cities and towns in which great *tzaddikim* dwelt, she would have him knock on their doors and beg them for a blessing for children. Kasriel and Breindel had amassed a huge quantity of such blessings, but it was as if a thick iron door stood between these blessings and G-d's Holy Throne.

One day Kasriel spoke to Breindel of an upcoming journey. She realized that his route would take him close to the city of Koznitz.

Breindel would not pass up the opportunity. "You must go to the holy *Maggid* of Koznitz. I'm sure the blessing of such a man wouldn't go unheard."

Kasriel promised, and so when he neared Koznitz he entered the city for a short time, in order to visit the *Maggid*.

With tears in his eyes, the merchant told the holy *Maggid*, R' Yisrael of Koznitz, his terrible problem.

The *Maggid's* eyes seemed focused on some distant, invisible point. For a long while he was immersed in his lofty thoughts; Kasriel was certain that the *Maggid* was wafting through higher spheres of existence.

After a long, pensive silence the *tzaddik* nodded and said to the merchant, "Listen to me, Reb Yid, your story is not a simple one. I see a very serious claimant against you, who is keeping you from having children. But I can't get to the root of it, and no matter how hard I tried to cancel it I have not succeeded. I only see one possibility for you: Travel to Lublin, to the *Chozeh*, whose eyes see all. I'm sure he'll be able to tell you clearly what must be done."

And so it was: The merchant immediately set off to the Rabbi of Lublin.

The *Chozeh* asked him, "Did you have any ties to another woman before your current marriage?"

"Yes."

"And who broke the engagement?"

"I did," Kasriel answered uncomfortably, though he could not understand what the Rabbi was leading up to, and why he had this sudden interest in matters long forgotten.

"And did you ask the woman whom you shamed for forgiveness?" the *Chozeh* asked.

Kasriel's entire body shook. It had never occurred to him, nor to his father, to ask his fiancée's forgiveness. They had cast her aside like a broken plate, no longer needed. R' Menashe had declared that the entire agreement was null and void; he made a match with a wealthy man, not with a bankrupt pauper whose possessions were already gone by the time they announced the engagement. After all, Shalom Shachna had simply covered up his hopeless financial situation.

Now the *Chozeh* of Lublin told him sternly, "Know that the shamed bride's sorrow and tears have created a terrible indictment against you in Heaven, and as a result it has been decreed that you should have no children."

Kasriel, like a hurt child, burst out in tears. "Isn't there any hope? Am I doomed to die childless?"

The *Chozeh's* voice became soft and comforting. "No. You have one hope. If you ask forgiveness of the woman whom you wronged, the indictment will be removed."

The merchant's eyes lit up for a short moment, then darkened in despair once again. "Rebbe," he groaned, brokenhearted, "how will I find her? Twenty years have passed. No doubt she has married and taken on her husband's name. Can I go through every village and town, announcing, `Daughter of Shalom Shachna, wheat merchant of Cracow, I ask your forgiveness'? I still may not find her!"

The *Chozeh* of Lublin replied, "In three weeks the city of Balta holds its fair. Go to Balta and ask for a certain woman, a seller of straw baskets. And when you find her, ask her forgiveness for breaking the engagement."

Kasriel left all his business unattended. He altered his plans and made his way to the city of Balta. In his haste he reached it three days before the fair. He stayed in a reputable inn and spent the days wandering through the market area, wondering if the seller of baskets had arrived early too.

His failure to find the seller in the days before the fair he attributed to his early arrival. But when the third day of the fair had dawned, Kasriel was still wandering among the merchants and stalls, wending his way like a drunken man. He did not know what to do with himself, he was so worried and upset. No matter that many of his acquaintances and friends among the merchants saw him; no matter that he avoided their curious gazes and inquiries with obvious excuses; no matter that many of them thought he had gone mad.

Kasriel was ready to joyfully accept the tortures of humiliation. From his august position as one of the country's wealthiest men, he took on the role of a strange and bothersome man wandering around in search of a certain Mirel, who sold straw baskets, daughter of Shalom Shachna of Cracow, the bankrupt millionaire.

"An atonement for my sins," Kasriel murmured constantly to himself. "But what good will it do, all this humiliation, if I don't find my ex-fiancée and ask her forgiveness?"

At the end of the third day, with evening's shadows falling and the fair beginning to close up, Kasriel found himself on the edge of despair. His feet ached from the incessant walking and he longed to sit down and rest for a moment. In utter fatigue he collapsed on the side of the road, two tears of sorrow and hurt falling from his eyes.

In his bitterness he did not even notice the mass of threatening black clouds blowing in from the west. The sky, purpled hued from the sunset, grew dark in minutes; suddenly a bolt of lightning flashed, followed by a rumble of thunder. The sky opened: A drenching rain poured down. Kasriel woke from his reverie and raced to look for shelter. He hardly knew where he was going, and when he saw an open store he did not hesitate for a moment; he dashed inside.

Two women stood in the store, chatting. The saleswoman was showing her friend a large straw basket and praising its strength. Kasriel stood near the doorway listening intently for signs that the storm was abating, waiting to leave his shelter.

Suddenly he heard the saleswoman's voice. "Do you see the man standing in the doorway? He wants to run away. He's already run away from me once, leaving me to my fate. Now he wants to run away again."

Kasriel turned towards her. "Were you speaking of me?" he asked, his heart thumping.

"Certainly," came the smiling answer. "Don't you recognize Mirel, your former fiancée, the one whom you shamed and left without a word of explanation or apology?"

Kasriel slowly moved closer, his face aflame with embarrassment. "Forgive me," he begged her. "Believe me that I've been searching for you an entire week; I came here to find you."

"And where have you been for 20 years?" Mirel tormented him with her words.

With head hanging, Kasriel told Mirel of the events of the past decades, of his childlessness, of the words of the *tzaddikim* of Koznitz and Lublin and how they led him to her to ask her forgiveness, as the only means of nullifying the terrible decree against him.

His former betrothed listened to his words, from beginning to end. And then she spoke. "I am prepared to forgive you for the humiliation and shame that you heaped upon me. But only on one condition. I have a brother in the village of Verblank, about 400 miles from here, and he is in terrible distress. He must marry off his daughter, and he has nothing. If you travel to him and give him what he needs, I will forgive you."

Kasriel accepted her words fully. The next day he boarded his carriage for the journey to Verblank.

The trip took him a full month. The village was a tiny one, and hardly anyone had ever heard of it, but after considerable trouble he finally found it. When his carriage finally entered the outskirts of the town the rigors of the journey could be clearly seen upon it: Gone were the adornments and elegant appointments. Its axles squeaked, its wheels seemed ready to fall off, the shaft was broken. Like his carriage Kasriel, too, looked shattered and worn. He had never undergone such a difficult journey, but he accepted the judgment upon him, and ceaselessly whispered the words, "our troubles purify us."

When he reached the village he asked for the home of Yehudah, son of Shalom Shachna of Cracow. "Oh, Yehudah the leaseholder," one of the passersby said, "he lives in a small house on the northeastern corner of Verblank."

"If he is the leaseholder, he should have money. Why can't he marry off his daughter?" Kasriel wondered.

With difficulty his tired horses pulled the carriage to the tiny house.

A Jew of about 40 met him, his face alight with welcome. "Where are you from?"

"I've come from the fair in Balta," Kasriel answered, evading the question.

His host offered him food and drink. Eventually, they began to speak of personal things. Kasriel could tell that something was disturbing the leaseholder's serenity; he would occasionally give a deeply felt sigh.

"Reb Yehudah, why are you sad?" Kasriel asked.

The leaseholder let out still another sigh, almost a groan. "And if I tell you, will you be able to help me?"

Without answering directly, Kasriel encouraged him, "If a man has a worry in his heart, let him discuss it."

After a few moments the bleak picture became clear. The leaseholder was on the verge of marrying off his daughter, but a terrible blow had struck him. He had not been able to pay the landlord his annual rental fees, and the Graf had sent him off, taking away his sole means of sustenance. He did not have a penny with which to marry off his daughter.

"That's a small concern," Kasriel said. "How much do you need to marry off your daughter?"

"Two hundred zlotys."

"And what do you owe the Graf?"

"Another 200."

"And for a small sum such as that you're upset?" Kasriel laughed. "I'll give you 400 zlotys just to put a smile on your face."

His host looked at him as if he were crazy. "Have you come to tease me?" he asked angrily. "Don't I have enough troubles?"

Kasriel then told him that he was a rich merchant, and that he had met the man's sister, Mirel, in Balta, and she had sent him here to help her brother.

The man's face turned a bright red. "Not only are you making fun of me, you're also a liar. How can you have met my sister Mirel, when she's been dead for 15 years!"

Kasriel began to wonder. Perhaps he'd made a terrible error. "Are you Reb Yehudah, son of Shalom Shachna, the wheat merchant from Cracow?"

"I certainly am."

"And your sister Mirel was engaged to a boy named Kasriel, son of the forester R' Menashe?"

The leaseholder nodded and added, "I was already married then, and I never met the *chasan*, but I will never forget our humiliation. My sister never forgave her betrothed, not to the day of her death."

"But after her death, she has forgiven," the astounded merchant murmured, his hands trembling in fright.

"What?" Yehudah asked.

"I am that boy, Kasriel," he confessed, his voice choking. "I have been punished; for 20 years I am childless. Following the guidance of the Rebbe of Lublin I traveled to Balta and saw your sister there, and have received her forgiveness. And this is the proof: How else would I have known to come here?"

The man gave him a haunted look. "What was my sister wearing, and what did she look like?" he asked.

Kasriel described her in detail. Yehudah gave a shout. "It's true! That's exactly what Mirel looked like before her death, and she was wearing those clothes the day she passed away. The *Chozeh* of Lublin has brought my sister down from Above in order to grant you forgiveness and rescue me from my troubles."

Kasriel gave the man 400 zlotys he needed for the Graf and the wedding, and another hundred for himself. On his way home, he stopped in Lublin.

"Your journey has been successful," the *Chozeh* told him. "And this will be your sign: In a year from now, you will have a son of your own."

To Break an Engagement, and Not to Forgive

THE HOUSE WAS COMPLETELY SILENT. THE HEAVY METAL shutters had been pulled shut, as if trying to cast darkness down upon the melancholy tragedy taking place within. In days when all was well the house had been a lively place, with businessmen and scholars coming and going, and great rabbis and heads of yeshivahs arriving as daily visitors. This had been the nerve center, the meeting place of Jews from Lithuania, Russia, Poland, and other lands. This was the home of the Rabbi of the Diaspora — Rabbi Chaim Ozer!

R' Chaim Ozer Grodzinski was one of the leaders of his generation, the brilliant generation that preceded the Holocaust. He was President of the Council of Torah Sages at a time when that illustrious body was composed of the most venerable and revered

Torah sages. The eyes of world Jewry were constantly turned upon that humble house in Vilna. One word, one letter from him could move mountains.

Author of the book of responsa, *Achiezer,* replete with unusual genius and insight, R' Chaim Ozer had devoted himself entirely to the communal needs of his people. From an early age he was widely know as a respected *posek* and the Rav of Vilna, the "Jerusalem of Lithuania." All the issues that concerned Lithuanian Jewry were discussed in his home, and his word was law. Together with the *Imrei Emes* of Gur and Rabbi Shalom Ber of Lubavitch, he founded the organization Knesses Yisrael, to come to the aid of Russian Jewry in the year 5669 (1909).

It was no wonder, then, that R' Chaim Ozer's house was usually a hive of activity. R' Chaim Ozer bore the burden of the community as a mother carries her child; and somehow, he found time to deal with public matters, learn in unbelievable depth and breadth, and answer halachic questions put to him from the four corners of the earth, complex questions dealing with all sections of the *Shulchan Aruch.*

It was said of R' Chaim Ozer that when he stood to pray, his face would redden and be covered with splotches. Medical researchers investigating the unique phenomena explained that these came from his mammoth efforts to concentrate all his thoughts into his prayers, a monumental task for a brain as complex as his, but one he forced himself to take on because it was the halachah. He would put aside all other topics that were taking his attention and delve into the words of the prayers until, from the effort, his face would break out.

But now the house was silent. An unhealthy silence.

In one of the rooms R' Chaim Ozer's 12-year-old daughter lay in her sickbed. His only daughter had been stricken by a mortal illness. The family consulted the greatest specialists, but the girl's life flickered like a candle in the wind.

R' Chaim Ozer had no sons, and this daughter had been his

consolation and the apple of his eye. He and his wife had harbored the hope that one day she would marry one of Lithuania's greatest young scholars and enjoy a household blessed with many children.

News of the girl's fatal illness struck the Jewish world. Yeshivah students in every city stood in prayer, beseeching the Creator to have mercy on the daughter of the *gadol hador*.

In his distress R' Chaim Ozer sent a special messenger to Radin, to the venerable Chofetz Chaim, to beg him to intercede for his daughter, the light of his life.

The clatter of carriage wheels could be heard all along the road to Radin. The driver had been well paid for speed; he urged his horses on and whipped them mercilessly until they galloped into the small town.

The Chofetz Chaim was sitting in his tiny home, deeply involved in learning with his son R' Aryeh Leib, when the messenger burst in with his terrible news. "Save us, Rebbi, have mercy. R' Chaim Ozer's only daughter is mortally ill."

R' Aryeh Leib was terribly upset by the news. Trembling, he looked at his father's holy countenance to see how he would react.

Everyone knew of the great love that existed between R' Chaim Ozer and the Chofetz Chaim. All had heard the epigram of R' Chaim of Brisk: "The Chofetz Chaim hides his genius beneath his piety; R' Chaim Ozer hides his piety behind his genius."

In many of the difficult and complex issues that were brought before him, the Chofetz Chaim turned to the decisions and teachings of R' Chaim Ozer. He would say of him, "R' Chaim Ozer *is Klal Yisrael*."

R' Aryeh Leib was certain that if the terrible news had affected him so badly, how much more so would his father, the Chofetz Chaim, feel the anguish. He would certainly go to pray immediately, lock himself in his room, and beseech his Creator to send a cure for the ailing girl. After all, if R' Chaim Ozer was *Klal Yisrael*, his only daughter was no private individual. She was the *daughter* of *Klal Yisrael!*

To his son's consternation, the Chofetz Chaim did not react at all. He accepted the news tranquilly, and merely said, "May G-d have mercy."

And nothing else.

He did not ask for the sick girl's name and the name of her mother, in order to pray for her. He did not ask for details of the illness.

R' Chaim Ozer's messenger on one side, and R' Aryeh Leib on the other, were perplexed. The messenger recovered his composure first. He approached the Chofetz Chaim and whispered into his ear, "She is R' Chaim Ozer's daughter."

A deep sigh escaped from the great man's heart. "I heard. May G-d have mercy."

R' Aryeh Leib could not take it any longer. "My dear father," he called out, "you can help the entire world, you can pray for any Jew who stands before you, but for your beloved R' Chaim Ozer, whom you yourself have called *Klal Yisrael,* for him you can do nothing? Why not?"

The old man sighed again, and said these mystifying words: "And is breaking an engagement nothing?"

The messenger and R' Aryeh Leib were silent. The suspicion grew within them: Perhaps the young woman had contracted a marriage secretly, and it had been broken. Was this what the Chofetz Chaim was referring to?

Without wasting another minute, the messenger galloped back to Vilna to pass on the strange words of the Chofetz Chaim to R' Chaim Ozer.

R' Chaim Ozer greeted the Chofetz Chaim's words with a look of astonishment. "I don't know what he's talking about. My daughter is so young, so far from marriage. What would make him think she would break an engagement, if she's never even been approached about a match?" The messenger pivoted around and went right back on the long journey to Radin. When he stood before the Chofetz Chaim once again, he told him of R' Chaim Ozer's reaction.

"Who's talking about the sick girl?" the Chofetz Chaim answered. "Let the father of the child examine himself. Was he not once engaged as a youth, and didn't he break the engagement? His former fiancée has not yet forgiven him, and because of her R' Chaim Ozer is being punished."

When the messenger, after some days, returned to Vilna with the words of the venerable sage, R' Chaim Ozer shuddered and wrung his hands. "Now I finally understand the depth of the Chofetz Chaim! Yes, when I was a youth my father, R' Dovid Shlomo Grodzinski, sent me to learn in the yeshivah in Volozhin. When I grew of age I became engaged to a certain woman from a town close to Volozhin, but for various reasons the connection was broken."

And now it was clear whose forgiveness was lacking.

His daughter's illness grew worse by the hour. R' Chaim Ozer did not hesitate for even one day. The words of the Chofetz Chaim were, to him, a command from Heaven.

He made every effort to find out where his former betrothed lived but, despite his connections throughout the entire land, he had to expend considerable energy until he was finally able to discover her address and married name.

On the day that he received all the details of the woman, he left to speak with her, covering part of the route by train and part by horse-drawn carriage. After two days and a night he arrived, exhausted, at the woman's home.

The man of the house was shocked by the sight of his notable guest. R' Chaim Ozer was still quite young, with only a few gray hairs in his beard, yet his fame had spread throughout Lithuania.

"To what do I owe this honor?" he asked respectfully.

"I'd like to speak with your wife," R' Chaim Ozer answered.

The host took a few awe-filled steps back and entered the kitchen to call his wife, whom their exalted guest was awaiting. But his wife's reaction when she stood before the great man was so unexpected that he was left dumbstruck, staring at a scene that he couldn't believe.

The woman had immediately recognized her guest, but no trace of surprise passed over her face, which remained hard and unmoving. It seemed that she had been waiting for this for a long, long time, and had prepared well for it. "What do you want from me?" she asked frostily.

R' Chaim Ozer understood from her tone that her former fury still burned within her. The head of all Diaspora Jewry stood before her, conciliating her with soft words, explaining that he had not, Heaven forbid, ever meant to insult her or her family, but for a certain reason they had had to part and go their own separate ways. Brokenhearted, he asked her forgiveness, head bent and spirit humbled. He told her of his daughter's serious condition and begged her, for the sake of G-d, to forgive him fully.

The woman stared at him, her eyes flashing thunderbolts.

"What are you talking about? You think you've insulted me, that you threw me away like an empty pot? Just the opposite: I'm thrilled that you left me!"

Another man might have understood her words to mean that all was well. If, after all, there had been no insult, there could be no need for forgiveness. But R' Chaim Ozer, one of the wisest men of his time, knew better: The truth was the exact opposite. He again repeated his arguments and asked for mercy. His daughter's very life was at stake!

"I don't know what you want," the woman repeated, looking at his complete discomfiture with satisfaction. "I didn't need you or your kind. My esteemed husband, may he live and be well, stands head and shoulders above you!"

Her husband stared at his wife as one would look at someone insane. He, an average scholar, was being compared to Lithuania's greatest genius?

R' Chaim Ozer's face fell and his shoulders drooped. He understood that the decree had been sealed. The woman refused to forgive him. With a heavy heart he left to Vilna.

When he returned home he was not surprised to hear that his daughter's condition had worsened during his absence, and that she now hovered close to death.

The girl lay on her sickbed for a few more days. When her last hours approached, R' Chaim Ozer shut himself up in his room to write dozens of urgent letters regarding matters of halachah and communal problems that could not be delayed. Every so often he would race to his dying daughter's room to check on her condition.

"How can it be?" one of the men close to him asked. "How can a father whose only child is dying leave her bedside to sit and write letters?"

"I have no choice," R' Chaim Ozer answered, his face wreathed in a holy light, "I know that in a short while I will be an *onen* and will not be allowed to do anything. And what will be of the community? Why should so many people have to suffer because of my own personal tragedy?"

(With thanks to my brother, R' Chanoch Chaim shlita of Ashdod, who told me this poignant story, heard from one of the gedolei hador.)

To Survive Two World Wars

PART 1:

THE WEISSMAN FAMILY LIVED IN THE CITY OF SLOBODKA. There were two brothers, R' Yerachmiel and R' Menashe, both respected merchants who earned a fine living.

The First World War, which broke out on Tishah B'Av of 5674 (1914), cast all of Poland into chaos and transformed everyone's life. The Weissman brothers and their families, together with all the Jews of Slobodka, were exiled and sent into the depths of Russia.

R' Yerachmiel Weissman was a robust man, but the rigors of the journey took their toll and left him broken. He felt too weak to even take up his trade, as he had done so successfully in the past. The family had a very difficult adjustment to life in the forgotten Russian town. They soon fell into dire poverty and made the acquaintance of its terrible companion — searing hunger.

"Dovid, my son," R' Yerachmiel turned to his eldest, a youth of 12, "you're a smart boy. You see that I can't take care of the family. We have no choice: You must go out to work and bring back a few rubles or we will all die of starvation."

Dovid Weissman was very mature for his years. He did not hesitate; that very day he went out to wander through the city streets. After spending some hours outside he came to a conclusion: The goods most wanted in the city were cigarettes.

In those days cigarettes were sold singly, not in packs, and they were relatively expensive. Youngsters would walk through the streets holding wooden trays hanging from leather straps slung over their shoulders. The tray contained a metal box filled with tobacco leaves and piles of thin paper. If a man wanted to buy a cigarette, the boy would place some leaves on the paper, roll it tightly and paste it down. Boys who had earned a few rubles would invest their profits in a small box that made it easier to roll the cigarettes. The box had a groove in which they would place the paper and tobacco. When they would close the lid the paper would roll around the leaves and paste itself down, leaving a product that looked almost like it was factory rolled.

Dovid borrowed a few rubles from his cousin Yosef, who was a year older than he. He bought all the necessary equipment and began selling cigarettes in the streets of the city. He had good luck, and sold 30 cigarettes on the very first day. He doubled the number on the second day of work, and within a short time had turned into a successful hawker of cigarettes.

The profits from his work sustained his family for a few months; his earnings were a mere pittance, but were enough to buy basic foodstuffs such as flour, potatoes, barley, and even an occasional loaf of bread.

One day, as Dovid stood on the frigid street, one of his steady customers, Vadim Bilitzki, a highly placed army officer whose many medals adorned his chest, stopped and asked Dovid to roll a few cigarettes for him.

"How many, two or three?" Dovid asked. Vadim was a good customer, who always paid, even before receiving the merchandise.

Vadim hesitated. "I need a lot this time. Your entire stock."

"What?" the boy was surprised. "Why?"

Vadim looked despondent. "I'm off to the battlefield, my boy. I won't be here for the next few weeks."

The boy was overcome with a wave of happiness. Wonderful, today he would not have to wander through the freezing streets until nightfall. Another few minutes and he would be able to return home with his day's profits.

He worked energetically and diligently, filling dozens of papers with tobacco and rolling them carefully.

When he finished rolling 100 cigarettes the soldier opened a large bag and poured the contents of the tray inside. Dovid looked at him, eagerly awaiting payment. "I've got no money to give you right now," Vadim said hastily. "When I come back from the war, I'll give you all I owe you. You know me; I'm no thief."

"What do you mean when you come back? Who knows if you'll return alive?"

"Let's hope for the best," the soldier called over his shoulder as he walked swiftly away.

Dovid ran after him. "Sir!" he shouted, crying. "Give me at least a little of the money. You've left me with nothing! I don't even have enough to buy tobacco tomorrow."

Vadim did not stop. "I'm sorry, youngster, but I have nothing either. Don't worry, I promised I'd return it. I'll keep my word."

"Then give me back the cigarettes!" Dovid yelled furiously, balling his fists. Bilitzki did not respond, just walked quickly away.

Dovid returned to his home shaking with anger. He threw himself down on the floor and wept tears of despair and fury. Then he told his family of the theft. "Now we'll all die of hunger," he wailed. "The soldier took everything!"

R' Yerachmiel would not let his son fall into the cold arms of despair. "And what did you start with?" he asked gently. "You started with nothing also! G-d, Who helped you the first time, will help you again."

And indeed in the following days Dovid slowly built up his stock again. First a good friend lent him a few kopeks, then he earned a little profit. The trade grew and after a few months Dovid was again doing brisk business.

A few years passed. The First World War came to an end. The Polish and Lithuanian refugees began to return to their homes. The Weissman family, too, wandered the crowded roads. When they reached the capital city of Moscow they could go no further. Moscow now was crammed with thousands of exiles and refugees, and the Russian rail system, with its hundreds of miles of track, was collapsing beneath the weight of their numbers.

Dovid Weissman, now 16, found himself trapped once again. In Moscow they sold cigarettes in shops; there was nothing for him to do here.

The two Weissman brothers and their families sat in a miserable hovel in Moscow, hungry and tired. Dovid was the first to rouse himself. "We can't go on like this. We've got to earn a living somehow," he said, and he walked out into the city's streets.

"Wait! Let me go with you," his cousin Yosef, 17, called out.

First they searched together for some means of sustenance, in vain. Moscow was full of hungry people, beggars wandering the streets in search of food or a job, any job, anything to stave off starvation.

"We've got to separate," Dovid said after a fruitless search of several hours. "You go right, and I'll go left."

And so the two went their separate ways. Dovid, who was always lucky, found a deserted Russian church with a large apple tree growing in its courtyard. He looked to and fro, saw that no one was watching, and within seconds had climbed the tree and picked several red, succulent apples, which he hid in his pockets.

He sold the apples for a good price, bought bread and some other foodstuffs, and returned home by evening, happy with his treasure.

When he walked into the house he saw the melancholy faces of his family. They answered his unspoken question, telling him that eyewitnesses had brought back the news that Dovid's cousin

Yosef had been pulled in by uniformed members of the dreaded secret police, the GPO.

These were the days of the Bolshevik revolution. Yosef had been wearing his Jewish identity proudly, with two long *peyos* flowing unconcealed. Apparently, his Jewish appearance had aroused the wrath of the Communist policemen, who had been commanded to eradicate all signs of religion in Russia.

R' Menashe was on the verge of collapse. He knew that whoever entered the GPO headquarters never left it alive, unless it was to travel to Siberia.

Only Dovid managed to inject a ray of hope within the family. First he made certain that they ate some of the bread he had brought. Then he tried to console his uncle, though his words made little impression on the distraught parent.

The next day Dovid went back to the tree. A few dozen apples had remained upon it, and he hoped to pick them. As he stood in the abandoned churchyard he realized what had happened. This, too, was a religious institution, and though the atheistic government had come down most harshly upon its Jews, it had persecuted other religions as well. No doubt this unholy sanctum had fallen victim to it.

He again checked to make certain no one could see him. He climbed up to a branch, filled a sack that he had brought, and returned to the ground.

A heavy hand fell upon his shoulder. Dovid's heart almost stopped beating. He raised his eyes in fear and saw the stony face of a beefy Russian officer who towered over him. "Hey, kid!" he sneered. "You're a thief! Come along with me to the police station." The officer's hands held him in a grip of steel. He pulled Dovid out of the courtyard and began to walk with him; the ground seemed to shake beneath the Russian's heavy footsteps.

The soldier and Dovid walked together for a few moments. They reached a narrow street. Dovid's heart pounded. "I'm doomed, just like my cousin Yosef," he thought in despair.

Suddenly the officer broke out in hearty laughter. "I really had you scared," he chortled like a child. "Don't you recognize me?"

Dovid recovered from his paralyzing fear and stared at the

Russian's face. Suddenly he remembered. "You're Vadim Bilitzki!" he said in a voice that mixed joy with a tinge of suspicion.

"That's me!" Vadim gave another throaty laugh. "A few good years have passed since I made off with your cigarettes, right? What are you doing here, stealing apples in Moscow?"

Dovid told him how he had come to this difficult situation. "I have to take care of my entire family," he explained.

"I can help you," the soldier said excitedly. "I owe you a lot of rubles, and I'll pay you back with interest. Didn't I promise I would repay my debt?"

Dovid's brow furrowed in thought. He had a daring idea. He stared thoughtfully at the officer's uniform. "I'd rather make a trade with you. I'll forget about the money you owe; instead, get me my cousin Yosef, who was taken yesterday by the GPO."

Vadim was not overly enthusiastic. "Let me pay my debt and be done with it," he said. But Dovid remained adamant, and his steely will overcame the Russian's hesitation. "Okay, I'll help," he finally said, "only because I value a person with principles. If you're offering to give up the money during such difficult times just to get a relative out of jail, that's true brotherhood."

He took Dovid with him to the GPO headquarters. On the way he told Dovid that he actually was a member of the GPO. "You're lucky," he told Dovid. "I know them from within. Maybe I'll manage to find your cousin."

After crossing several busy boulevards they reached a quiet street. Dovid could not understand why it was so silent, in contrast to the busy flow of the neighboring avenues. But when he looked and saw the giant building looming over them he felt his heart stop. It was the most terrifying building in Moscow: GPO headquarters.

"I've entered the lion's den," Dovid thought as he crossed the threshold. "Will I ever come out alive?"

They walked through endless corridors, climbed up several stories, and reached the private office of Officer Vadim Bilitzki.

"Wait here," the officer said. "I'll go look for information on Yosef Weissman."

The minutes passed endlessly. Dovid sat, trembling in fear. Occasionally the door would open and officers would come in and go out. He was certain that one of them would call him. When the minutes turned into hours he was certain that the officer had led him into a trap.

After three hours, two men entered the room — Officer Bilitzki and Dovid's cousin Yosef, frightened but unharmed.

Vadim was a little impatient. "I had to use all my connections to find him in the cellar of the building. If a day or two had passed, he'd be dead!"

He accompanied the two out to the courtyard and advised them to get away quickly, before someone noticed them and started asking questions.

A few days later the Weissman family left Moscow behind and headed for Poland.

PART 2:

Twenty years passed.

Dovid Weissman left Slobodka, in the outskirts of Kovno, to live in a Polish town outside Lodz. He started a family and now had seven children, both sons and daughters. He was a healthy and robust man, a blacksmith by trade. After *Shacharis* he would go to his workshop and spend the day with metalwork, white-hot irons, and horseshoes.

One summer afternoon Dovid stood, a heavy hammer in hand, banging against a stubborn shoe that would not straighten out. The sound of the hammer drowned out all other noise, and so he did not hear the knocks on the smithy's iron door.

A bit more fire, a red-hot shoe, a coal-black forge — Dovid gave one last mighty blow and the piece of iron surrendered before him.

He stopped for a minute to rest, wiped the sweat off his brow with a dirty rag, and took a deep breath.

At that moment he heard the pounding of fists on his door. The hinges creaked and the door swung open. He turned and for a minute his face grew twisted with disgust. The man who stood before him in the doorway was not much to look at: a beggar of the most unsavory type, clothed in filthy rags, his fingernails long and blackened, his beard hanging unkempt, his hair overgrown and infested with lice.

"I'm hungry," the beggar said. "Do you have food for me?"

Dovid was overcome with abhorrence. "Why don't you go to the local soup kitchen? They give food there to anyone who needs it."

"I was there," the beggar answered wrathfully, "and they threw me out like a sick dog. They said I saw dark visions and it was forbidden to have mercy upon me."

At first Dovid, too, longed to grab the filthy beggar by the threadbare coat and throw him out. But his good heart immediately came to the fore.

"Yes. I do have food for you. What kind of a question is that? Come home with me and we'll eat a hearty lunch."

While he normally would not leave for home until nightfall, he locked up the workshop and took the beggar home. There he gave him food and drink and a new set of clothing. He heated up a large barrel of water and personally washed the beggar with soap from head to toe. He was not satisfied until he brought the beggar to a local barber to have his lice-infested hair cut off. After a good meal, a wash, and a haircut, the beggar looked like a new man.

After all this, the beggar sat, his face shining like the noonday sun. He gave his benefactor a strange look. "You've saved me; I was on the verge of death," he admitted. "What do you want in exchange?"

Dovid laughed. "What can you give me?"

The beggar's face grew serious. "Listen carefully to what I am going to tell you. In another year, a terrible war will break out. Airplanes will bomb all of Poland, the enemy will invade and destroy Poland. The majority of Poland's Jews will be massacred, and this town will be decimated. Only one family will remain — your family. The kindness that you have shown today will grant you life. You will be saved!"

Dovid looked at the man, his face a mask of conflicting emotions: disapproval, shock, pity. The beggar sitting across from him was mad, completely mad; still, one could not let him say such things. "Why are you talking like this?" he said. "You're not allowed to curse."

"It is not a curse," the beggar explained calmly. "It is the truth. Look at your calendar, mark the date in your memory, the 17th of Elul. In another year you will know that I was right."

Dovid remembered what the beggar had told him in the smithy. "Oh, that's why they threw you out of the soup kitchen. It was your cursing."

"Fools," the beggar snorted. "They do not have your merit. I wished to save the entire town through them. What do you want from me?"

"*Nebich*, what a shame, a madman," Dovid thought sadly.

The beggar stood up, his sack in hand. "The time is short. I see that you won't listen to me, but still I'll give you the keys to salvation. When the doom hits, say my name to yourself — Shraga Feivel ben Miriam — and you will be saved."

Without further ado, he left the house.

Dovid returned to his forge. With the first sound of iron smacking iron, he put the strange beggar out of his mind.

A year later, on Friday, the 17th of Elul 5699 (1939), the Second World War began. Dovid Weissman remembered the date; the words of the beggar, a hidden *tzaddik* it seemed, had come true. The planes of the Luftwaffe soared over Polish skies, dropping thousands of bombs that razed buildings completely and cut a swathe of death and devastation on the ground.

After several days the Nazis, may their names be blotted out, arrived in Dovid's town. They made their headquarters in a large building and that night began their *aktion*.

Soldiers marched from street to street, microphones in hand, calling all the residents to pack their things and gather together in the market square, near Nazi headquarters.

The majority of the town's panic-stricken residents did as they were told; they had seen enough of their satanic conquerors to know what would happen if they did not listen to them. They gathered in the square, were jammed together like animals onto packed trucks, and sent immediately to the death camps that masqueraded as labor camps.

Dovid gazed out of his window at what was going on outside, his wife and children staring at him with large questioning eyes.

He was in a terrible quandary. His quick mind realized that these people were being sent to a place from which no one ever returned; the evil faces of the Nazis left little doubt of their intentions.

Suddenly he remembered the words of the beggar, the hidden saint. "I'll be back in a minute," he told his family, and he locked himself into the bedroom. He closed his eyes and concentrated mightily on trying to remember the beggar's name. Finally he murmured, "Master of the Universe, dearest Father in Heaven, save us in the merit of having helped the hidden *tzaddik*, Shraga Feivel ben Miriam."

At that moment he had the clear feeling that his prayer had been answered. He felt as if the *tzaddik* were standing by his side instructing him:

"Don't go to the market. Whoever goes will be sent to his death." The thought passed through his mind, as clear as a spoken word.

"But what will I do?" A second thought came to him. "If I don't go, the soldiers will come into my house and kill us all."

"No. Behind the door is a very high ladder," again, an unbidden thought flashed through his brain. "Take it and use it to hide in the Nazi headquarters! An ancient saying said: 'If you're looking for a way to escape from the lion, hide in his den.' In back of the building there is a small entrance to the attic; the family can climb up there and hide until the fury is over."

Again, his thought responded: "But won't they see us as we walk outside? Look at the street; it's deadly out there."

Another response: "'They have eyes, but do not see.' Just go."

When he returned to the other room and told his wife and children what he planned to do, they could not believe what their father, usually so logical and careful, was saying. But Dovid was not asking their approval, and with perfect faith he went out to the courtyard and picked up the ladder. He carried it to Nazi headquarters in complete tranquility. His family snuck behind him with hesitant steps. They were certain that at any moment a Nazi soldier would catch them in the act of escaping.

The beggar's promise was kept: No one saw them. On one side

the Nazis were gathering together all the town's populace; occasionally the sound of gunfire could be heard, followed by a scream and the thud of a falling body. All the while Dovid and his family publicly carried out their escape. They leaned the ladder against the building, climbed up one by one, and when they had all reached a concealed place on the roof, pulled up the ladder behind them.

A beseeching voice came from below. "Please, dear Jews, let me climb up too."

In the courtyard stood a young man in chassidic garb. Dovid did not recognize him. He hesitated for only a moment and then slid the ladder down.

The boy climbed up and reached the roof. He was as white as the cement blocks of the building. Strangely, he did not look at his benefactors, nor did he offer a word of thanks. He immediately sat down in a corner, withdrew into himself, and began to recite *Tehillim*.

The villains had already taken 10 truckloads laden with their human cargo out of the village, but their bloodlust was not assuaged. They wondered if anyone remained in hiding. A special microphone blasted through the streets of the town commanding anyone who had not turned up to do so immediately. "Whoever comes, receives the gift of life. But anyone found hiding will be killed immediately."

Dovid heard the threat and believed it. He grabbed the ladder and walked towards the attic entrance.

"Let's go down," he told his family. "You heard what they said. Let's save ourselves."

At that moment the microphone stood directly beneath them. The announcement was repeated. The new threat ended all hesitation: Dovid Weissman and his family walked towards the roof.

The chassidic young man was deep in his *Tehillim*, his devout gaze riveted to the pages of the small volume. Suddenly he lifted his eyes and stared at Dovid Weissman and his family as they made their way to the entrance to give themselves up to the Nazis. With a lightning swift leap he reached the doorway and blocked their way with his thin body.

"What are you doing?" Dovid asked, surprised. "Let us go down."

The boy was adamant. "You're not leaving here," he said firmly.

"Who asked you what we should do, *chassid*?" Dovid hissed angrily. "I saved you and you didn't even say thank you. Now don't stand in our way."

But the youth did not budge an inch. His lean body stood firm before them like an unyielding boulder. Dovid tried to push him away without success; that emaciated frame was like steel. With anger and impatience Dovid finally sat down and asked the young man, "Why are you sticking your nose into something that doesn't concern you?"

"Because you're committing suicide!" the youth shouted. "You can stay here. No one knows that you are here. Going down means certain death."

"How do you know?" Dovid demanded. "They say the opposite: Whoever is found hiding will be killed, and whoever gives himself up will be allowed to live."

The youth gave him a piercing glance. "You believe those man-beasts? Soon you'll see their deeds with your own eyes."

Dovid carefully peeked downwards. His village, bustling with life and joy, looked like a ghost town. A thick silence hung over it; there was no sign of life. Only the echo of the Nazi laughter could be heard coming from all sides, the demonic laughter of the Satan.

A woman who heard the announcement left her hiding place in her cellar and walked out confidently. "Here I am," she said hopefully. "You look like fair men, the most cultured in Europe. I'm certain we can trust you. I'm sure —"

The shot ripped through the air, felling her in mid-sentence.

There was a second's silence and then the blonde soldiers began to laugh once again, a cruel, mocking laughter. The officers wore proud smiles as they approached to examine their handiwork.

White faced, Dovid and his family walked back inside, to the warm shelter of the attic. The chassidic youth was back in his corner, busy with his *Tehillim*.

The *aktion* was over before noon. The village was now *Judenrein*, free of Jews. The officers and soldiers again examined every house and finally left. Only one building was not searched — their headquarters. And thus Dovid Weissman and his family were left alive, the sole refugees of an entire Jewish city that had been wiped off the face of the earth without leaving a trace.

Now they were faced with a new question: What to do now? Hunger, too, was making itself felt. Dovid considered all the possibilities and decided to get out and join the large Jewish community of Lodz.

Again, it was the chassidic youth who stood in his way. "The Jews of Lodz, too, have been sentenced to death. Don't go there."

Dovid began to wonder if there wasn't something strange about this *chassid*. He was not from the village. How had he come to be there? Why had he so adamantly kept Dovid from descending the ladder? How did he know that Dovid would witness the Nazi cruelty even before it happened?

Dovid Weissman was a steel-tempered, firm man, possessed of a clear and straightforward mind. But in times of stress it was his stubbornness that got the better of him. He pushed the youth away, slid the ladder down, and descended with his family to the courtyard to begin the two-hour journey to Lodz.

"Don't go!" the boy beseeched him. "Have pity on your family. You'll stay alive in any case, but what of your children?"

Dovid stopped in his tracks, looked behind him and said, "What are you trying to tell me?"

The young man came down the ladder and caught up to him. "If you stay here, you'll all be saved and will merit going up to *Eretz Yisrael*. If you go to Lodz, only you will survive."

"Foolishness," Dovid looked at him in mockery. "Are *chassidim* also prophets? You may see into the heavens, but I see reality. If we stay here we'll die of hunger, and in Lodz we'll find food and shelter."

And so they began their journey. The boy followed behind them for a time, but eventually disappeared, as if he had vanished into the air.

Dovid did not pay attention. He was burdened by the terrible hunger that was overcoming his family. They rushed towards Lodz with the last of their strength, but when they reached it they were horrified to find that all the Jews had been gathered into one ghetto. Jewish kapos guarded the gates around the ghetto. Dovid began to argue with them: He wanted permission to enter to see if it was worth his staying there or not. The guards were not used to such defiance and they tried to capture Dovid, who returned their blows with his own.

Finally, Dovid decided to give in. He let himself be led inside, where he was brought to the Jew appointed as leader of the ghetto. The ghetto leader made it clear to Dovid that there was no choice: He had to report his arrival to the authorities. But if Dovid did so willingly, he would be given certain benefits. Dovid was eventually sent to work in a shoe factory that manufactured boots for the Nazi soldiers; his family was given certain privileges.

After a few months, the situation changed completely. The Nazis systematically liquidated the Lodz ghetto. Dovid Weissman's wife and children were sent to the death camps, never to return, just as the chassidic youth has foretold. Dovid himself wandered from camp to camp, but somehow eluded the gas chambers. He used to ask himself how long his robust constitution could hold out, not realizing that he had long since become a walking skeleton, his once-rosy cheeks yellowed and dried out, eyes buried deep in their sockets, shaved head nodding back and forth like a balloon slowly losing its air.

The war drew to a close. The Nazis had retreated to Germany before the Allied troops, taking with them tens of thousands of these walking scarecrows on a brutal death march that began in the countries of eastern Europe and ended in the valley of tears itself — the cursed land of Germany.

They had already reached this land of Amalek, Dovid Weissman among them. A zombie, lacking all interest in life, he staggered like a drunken man, often feeling that he was on the verge of falling. From such a fall one did not stand up again; the Nazis shot anyone who could not march.

But two men stood by him, two men like angels; two men who wandered with him from the Belzitz concentration camp: at one side, Michoel Stroichlitz, at the other Pinya Adler. They encouraged him ceaselessly and called to him, "Come along, Dovid. We've almost reached safety." "Don't give up, Dovid. The Nazis are on the verge of defeat."

Their calls to him came from behind a thick curtain of fog. He walked blindly, a robot, one kilometer, another, and another. His feet stumbled over a rock and he tripped, but each time Michoel and Pinya grabbed his arms, two long matchsticks with a blue tattooed number scorched into one of them.

It was a battle between life and death, and Dovid was choosing death.

His legs bumped into a large stone that seemed to have been waiting just for him. He staggered and suddenly fell out of the straight line of thousands of men.

A Nazi soldier, Johann Schultz, who had been marching next to them, escorting them from Poland, was prepared, his truncheon in his hands. What was this? To fall out of line, to break the wondrous German efficiency?

The truncheon struck at Dovid Weissman's head. Dovid fell to the side of the road, a dead weight.

He could feel himself soaring upwards, light and free, liberated from the burden of the evil kingdom whose men had sucked out his blood for so many years. He was being pulled towards a luminous light that gave off a feeling of infinite beauty and serenity. Would he want to stay here, the light asked, or return to his body below?

He looked downwards, his heart filled with pity, at the yellowed skeleton left broken on the snow-covered field by the road. "What have I from this miserable form?" he asked the source of the light. "It's good here, and pleasant. Why should I suffer more?"

"These dry bones will live once again," the source told him in a wordless communication. "There are still things left for you to do in the world: Return to your body."

And in the passing of a millisecond Dovid opened his eyes and saw Michoel Stroichlitz and Pinya Adler rubbing his wrists with snow to awaken him.

"Don't despair, Dovid," they covered him with a mantle of true love, the love for a fellow Jew that is endless and deep. "Wake up, strengthen yourself; salvation is near."

An unnatural strength lifted him from the snow. Dovid walked on.

PART 3:

Dovid and thousands of other Jews in Bergen-Belsen wandered through Germany itself until the war's end. His two benefactors, Stroichlitz and Adler, were separated from him, and Dovid never saw them again.

The British army liberated Bergen-Belsen on Monday, 2 Iyar, 5705 (1945). The British soldiers found Dovid on the verge of death. He was skin and bones and sunken, lifeless eyes, nothing more. He was fed a warm bean soup day after day, cared for by devoted doctors who infused new life into him. After a few months his body recovered its former strength.

Dovid spent more than a year wandering through Germany. He became part of the "Revenge Squad," men who sought vengeance and quietly destroyed several of the demon's willing henchmen. They would seek out Nazi soldiers who had tortured them, make certain of their guilt, and then come to strike.

Johann Schultz's name, too, appeared on their list. The devoted Nazi soldier, who bludgeoned so many during the death march, had left the army and was living peacefully in Hamburg. Dovid and his colleagues found him, waited for him in ambush, and fell upon him mercilessly. Dovid hit him wildly, screaming, "This is for Dovid Weissman! This is for the blow on my head. Why? What did I do to you?"

Schultz would have died beneath their hands, but neighbors heard his screams and came to his rescue before they could let loose their wrath upon him.

A few years after the war was over, Dovid Weissman reached *Eretz Yisroel*. Slowly he built a new life: married, bought a home in

Rishon LeTziyon. He saw a new generation born to him, sons and daughters to fill the place of those massacred by the Nazis. Again he took up the blacksmith's trade but this time unsuccessfully: He became entangled in failing agricultural businesses and found himself facing enormous debts. He saw no way out of the swamp in which he had fallen, and there were days when he longed for death.

A policeman came to his home one afternoon. Dovid's heart began to thump wildly. "Come with me to the station," the representative of the law ordered. Dovid accompanied him, rehearsing in his mind dozens of explanations for his financial troubles. He had no doubt that they would find him guilty; only one thing remained: to confess and ask for a light sentence.

To his surprise he was brought to a top officer who showed him a letter he'd received from Germany's Ministry of the Interior.

Dovid could not believe it. It seemed that Johann Schultz had actually traced him all the way here and was demanding that he return to Germany to face charges of having beaten him, leaving him totally disabled.

"You don't have to travel to Germany," the policeman explained. "Israel has no extradition treaty with them. If you go, Germany must take care of all your traveling expenses, put you up in good lodgings, and provide you with an attorney. If you lose, you might have to go to a German prison."

"I'm going," Dovid made the decision on the spot. "I'm not afraid of him."

The trial took place in Hamburg, Johann Schultz's city. Dovid refused the services of a lawyer, preferring to represent himself. The indictment denied any guilt on Schultz's part, claiming that Johann Schultz had not been part of Weissman's group, and that Dovid's claim of Schultz's blow to his head was a lie. The indictment claimed that Dovid had taken an innocent German citizen and disabled him completely. There was no lack of eyewitnesses: All of Johann's neighbors testified how the defendant had hit

Johann while shouting, "This is for Dovid Weissman."

Dovid stood fearlessly on the defendant's platform. He took advantage of the scene and transformed himself from accused to accuser, turning the federal courtroom into a stage watched closely by the legions of journalists who came to view the unusual trial.

For three days Dovid unfolded the story of the tortures that he and his family had undergone from the outbreak of the war until its end, which left him the only survivor of an entire city. The Weissman family became a microcosm for all of European Jewry, the story of a nation which had lost one third of its people.

At the end of his extended testimony the judge said, "You have touched me greatly, and almost persuaded me of your innocence. Only one vital detail is missing from your testimony: If you can give me the names of some Jews who were with you in the death march, we can clarify if Johann Schultz was in charge of your transport."

Dovid almost collapsed on the spot. This evil man had found a way of discrediting his testimony. "Twenty years have passed since then. How can I remember someone who was with me for such a short time?"

"Be that as it may," the judge said sternly, "we are a methodical people. In our archives we have the lists of transports sent to the death camps. These include the death marches. We also have the names of the soldiers who accompanied them. Your testimony hinges on this: If you can give us some names, you will win this judgment, and be awarded a huge compensation. If not, you will be sentenced to jail for many years."

The blood left Dovid's face. He felt the seriousness of the moment, and his knees began to buckle. The courtroom whirled around him; hundreds of eyes stared hungrily at him.

Suddenly he felt his lips moving. "Master of the Universe, save me in the merit of Shraga Feivel son of Miriam. Save me!"

And suddenly he again felt that strange feeling, just as he had felt during the first hours of the war. The forgotten names jumped out from the deep recesses of his memory.

Dovid shook himself, as if from a deep sleep. "Will two names suffice?"

"Yes," the judge said mockingly.

"Michoel Stroichlitz and Pinchas Adler accompanied me on that last march from Belzitz."

The courtroom was filled with whispers. "The matter will be investigated," the judge announced, banging his gavel.

Dovid Weissman returned home, victorious. He was awarded damages of hundreds of thousands of German marks, while Johann Schultz was brought to the police for investigation of his war crimes.

Not long after he settled all his financial affairs, Dovid sent a letter to one of the great Chassidic leaders of the generation, asking for his blessing for the future.

The rebbe added these words to his blessing: "I am filled with wonder at a Jew who managed to undergo all you've gone through. There is no doubt that in the merit of your remarkable kindness you stayed alive through two world wars."

(With special thanks to R' Avraham Moshe Kipper of Jerusalem, who told this story as he had heard it directly from the protagonist. Certain details and names have been changed.)

He Who Laughs First

IF SOMEONE HAD TOLD PROFESSOR HEINZ BAUER THAT ONE day he would be counted among the *chassidim* of the holy Rebbe, R' Shlomo HaKohen of Radomsk, author of the *Tiferes Shlomo*, he would undoubtedly have broken out into hearty laughter, as if he had heard a particularly good joke. Or perhaps he would have erupted into a raging fury, as a reaction to such an outrageous suggestion. It all would have depended on his mood at that moment.

For it was impossible to imagine a greater contrast than Professor Bauer and *Chassidus*. According to the honorable professor, it was like east versus west, with each in its own corner. He was wreathed in the glow of enlightenment and progress; he had no connection with "the unenlightened primitives, still living in the Dark Ages."

Heinz Bauer, enlightened among the enlightened, was born in a home filled with refinement and culture in the capital city of Berlin. His education reflected the mores of German cultural values. His parents had been born to *shomer Shabbos* families, but they had each left observance in their youth. It had been a time of the flourishing of the Enlightenment, and many young people had followed its teachings blindly. In order to hold on to one's beliefs in those hard days, one had to be possessed of an iron-clad personality and unyielding will to swim against the stream. Such young people were rare, and the vast majority of German Jewish youth followed the "enlightened dawn," seeing their Jewish world as a phenomenon whose time had come and gone.

Heinz Bauer's parents had flung their Jewish beliefs behind them, and Heinz, their only child, was never nourished with the rich traditions of his fathers. He grew up completely ignorant of Torah, entirely devoid of Jewish knowledge.

But it would be misleading to say that he had been taught

absolutely nothing; he was given some vague, erroneous knowledge, all of it negative and ugly. He was told of his brethren growing up in eastern Europe, and that they resembled the primitive tribes of deepest Africa.

Heinz excelled in his classes in elementary and high school, thanks to his extraordinary talents and unparalleled diligence. No one was surprised, therefore, when he was accepted into the elite University of Berlin. If not for top scholars like Heinz, after all, for whom was the university created?

The Jewish student Bauer did well in his studies. His lineage did not stand in his way, and upon graduation the university staffers recommended that the rector appoint him a lecturer in the university itself!

On the day that Heinz put on his square, black lecturer's cap, its tassel hanging down behind him, his parents were overcome with happiness. Could they have hoped for greater joy than this from their only child? Their life choices had truly justified themselves today: "How high could Heinz have reached if he'd kept his name, Chaim Bauer?" Siegfried Bauer whispered to his wife during the university's solemn installation ceremony. "Some antiquated chassidic court in Poland? Some obsolete yeshivah in Lithuania?" That world, they thought, belonged to a past that was no more.

Heinz Bauer made breathlessly swift progress; within five years he was a tenured lecturer whose classes were constantly popular; the best of the students concentrated thoughtfully on his every word. His home life too was one of joy: His young wife did all she could to advance her husband's career. Their son, Hans, was a lovely and bright youngster, the pride of his young parents. The future was rosy and promising. Heinz Bauer was the prime candidate for appointment as the next rector of the University of Berlin, a princely honor!

And then came the anonymous letter, sent to all the members of the university staff, accusing Heinz of unspeakable actions. The nominating process came to a halt; the university administration asked for some time to mull over the affair. Finally, Heinz was demoted to the position of junior lecturer.

His anger burned and seethed. He realized that some of his so-called friends, jealous of his success, had cooked up this foul stew behind his back. But all his attempts to deny the false accusations fell on deaf ears, and a junior lecturer he remained.

The troubles left his wife ill, and much to Heinz's distress, her sickness steadily became more and more severe. The doctors feared for her life, and recommended that she be taken immediately to the healing waters of the spa at Marienbad.

Heinz wandered the streets of Marienbad like one struck by lightning. With one sharp blow he had been cast from the glorious heights to the valley of shadow, his career shattered, his wife taken ill. None of the many watering places they tried did her any good. And if that was not enough, he was trapped here among odd-looking men who wore long black coats and jammed the pathways of the resort town, speaking their own strange language of Yiddish.

"How absurd," he thought to himself. "Another 20 or 30 years and there won't be a sign of them; a dream disappeared without a trace."

But the dream stubbornly refused to disappear from before him. Groups of *chassidim* strolled near him, and despite himself he heard fragments of their discussions. Through their Polish accents he was able to understand some of their words, and they piqued his curiosity.

"What do you think of the story of the German professor?" one older *chassid* asked another. Heinz jumped as if bitten by a scorpion. Were they talking about him? What did they possibly know about a German professor? He listened carefully, but much to his dismay he could not understand enough to piece together the story.

He approached the group. "Excuse me, but could I hear the story you've just told?"

Taken by surprise, the *chassidim* just stared at the young man who had the look of a gentile, and then turned their backs on him.

Calling after them, Heinz said, "I'm also Jewish, like you are." Saying these words for the first time in his life left him feeling somewhat confused. "I'm a professor in a university in Berlin, but a Jew. Could you tell me, please, the entire story."

A young man, the leader of the discussion, spoke slowly and carefully. He told of a professor in Germany whose wife was very sick. The doctors had despaired of her life. She came to the Rebbe of Radomsk, and the Rebbe told the professor that if his wife would begin to cover her hair, she would be healed. After a few weeks the professor had returned with the news: His wife, indeed, was covering her hair, and she was completely cured!

"The doctors were stunned, trying to figure out how the Rebbe knew something that had completely eluded them. They finally theorized that the sickness came from germs that lived in the woman's uncovered hair, and that by covering it the germs were destroyed."

"It's truly astounding," Heinz said, "It seems your rabbi is well versed in the healing arts."

He did not notice the smiles that his words aroused. The *chassidim* tried to correct him by explaining the religious significance of the head covering, but Heinz was lost in thought.

"Let me travel to Radomsk with you," he asked the group after a pensive moment. "My wife, too, is very sick."

The *chassidim* left Marienbad a few days later, in the company of an unusual guest, Professor Heinz Bauer. While he traveled, he left his wife in the city's large hospital, under careful medical supervision. These plans went against everything he had ever been taught, but he had no other options left; his wife was growing worse by the day and he held onto the story he had heard like a drowning man grabbing at straws. It was therefore with a heavy heart that he traveled to Radomsk. He hoped with all his heart that he would not return to his homeland and find himself a young widower.

The days of travel crumbled the foundations of his world view. The *chassidim* that he met did not act like barbarians, as he had been told all these years, and the cordiality that radiated from them was a phenomenon he had never encountered before. From his earliest youth he had grown up among stern men whose philosophy was never to show a hint of warmth or human emotion.

When he would return to Berlin one thing was certain. He would have to rethink his whole perspective, everything that his teachers and parents had taught him all these years. He waited impatiently for the meeting with the mysterious rabbi whom the *chassidim* spoke of with such boundless reverence. If the *chassidim* were so pleasant, how would their rabbi, who exemplified such fine manners, act?

But when his escorts brought him to the Rebbe's room, he was shocked by his reception. The Rebbe stood up and angrily asked his followers, "A gentile? You've brought a gentile here?"

"He's a Jew," one of the men stammered, "a professor from Berlin."

"We don't have enough gentiles in Poland, you had to bring me one from Germany?" the Rebbe thundered, as he scrutinized Heinz, with his smooth face and bare head, his stylish clothing and polished shoes.

"Rebbe, his wife is mortally ill," one of the men present tried to defend him.

"Come here," the Rebbe commanded. Heinz approached, his knees weak beneath him, towards the holy visage that stood before him. His heart thumped in fear.

"Your wife is sick?" the Rebbe asked. Heinz nodded.

The Rebbe lifted his hand and stroked Heinz's smooth cheeks once or twice. "And what are you?" the Rebbe growled at the professor. "A complete gentile!"

Heinz thought he would collapse from the humiliation, but the Rebbe showed him that he had not even begun to taste real shame.

"Place him on the table and give him a good whacking," the Rebbe ordered. The *chassidim*, who had been raised from babyhood to respect the sages, wasted no time, and they diligently beat the revered professor.

He did not even say goodbye to his newfound friends, he was so stunned and angry as he fled Radomsk. Could it be? They had actually hit him? Like a willful little boy? No, it seemed his parents and teachers were correct: The *chassidim* and their rebbes were a relic from the days before civilization.

Impatiently, Heinz rushed to the hospital, hoping at least to be able to see the wife of his youth one last time.

As he entered her room he felt that he was dreaming. His wife, terminally ill, was sitting peacefully in a chair reading, her pink cheeks glowing with good health.

"A miracle?" Heinz murmured weakly. "It's against nature."

"That's right," his wife said joyously. "That's what the doctors said. Such a total transformation takes place only one time in a million."

Heinz looked up alertly. He investigated, reckoned hours and days, and realized that the unexpected cure had taken place at those exact minutes that the Rebbe had stroked his cheek and the *chassidim* had beaten him.

"And if someone had told me that I was destined to become a *chassid* of Radomsk," old R' Chaim Bauer would tell his grandchildren many years later, "I would have laughed aloud. But to my good fortune, the One Who lives above laughed first."

Match and Rematch

R' ASHER OF STOLIN WAS A BOY OF 12 WHEN HIS father, R' Aharon "the Great," founder of Karlin *Chassidus*, was called to his Maker. R' Aharon's disciple, R' Shlomo of Karlin, took his Rebbe's place; at the same time, he also took young Asher into his home and raised him as his own child. R' Shlomo loved the boy and he used to say that the only reason he had come down to this world was to have a student such as Asher, to help him with his questions and understanding.

When R' Shlomo was called from this world in the year 5552 (1792), R' Asher began to lead the community. His *chassidim* loved him dearly, particularly those who lived in the city of Stolin, who were close to him physically as well as emotionally. People would come to see him, from great distances as well. By the end of his life, thousands were counted among his regular visitors, among them some who were not even *chassidim*.

There was one woman from Stolin who would push into the Rebbe's room quite often, each time bearing a request: Let the Rebbe bestow his blessing, on herself and her family, her husband, sons, and daughters. The woman slowly became a regular fixture in the household, recognized at once by the *gabbaim*. She would attach a sum to each of her written requests, a fairly large amount, and slowly her donations added up to a serious figure.

At first the Rebbe didn't say anything. He assumed that the woman's husband was not a *chassid*, that the man knew about his wife's visits to the holy court, and even if he did not want to join her he did not object to his wife getting a blessing from the *tzaddik* on his behalf. After all, what harm could it do?

But as her visits became more frequent, and as her donations increased, R' Asher's suspicions were aroused. He did not want to frighten off the woman, so he said nothing to her, but quietly sent his assistant to summon the husband.

"The Rebbe wants me?" the man said excitedly. He hastily slipped on his overcoat and walked quickly with the Rebbe's assistant. Not to be a *chassid*, never to visit the Rebbe, that was one thing; but when the Rebbe, in his glory, called you, that was something else entirely. What could the Rebbe possibly want?

Trembling, he sat near the doorway, waiting to be called in. He tried to solve the mystery, thinking of several possibilities and rejecting all of them. But what he was to hear from the Rebbe was indeed eye opening.

"Are you aware that your wife comes here often?' the Rebbe asked. The man answered in the affirmative, adding that though he was not enthusiastic about it, he was not against it either.

"And do you know that she gives me donations, large sums of money?" the Rebbe asked the man. This time his words fell like a thunderbolt. Money, a lot of money, had been disappearing; now the man knew where it was going. He had noticed it some time ago, but assumed his diligent wife had discovered a better hiding place for it than they had used before. Now it became clear: She had found the very best hiding place.

Slowly he shook his head, No!

The Rebbe looked carefully at the man's face; his pale hue told its own story.

"It seems I owe you this-and-this number of rubles." The Rebbe named an enormous sum. "But what can I do? I don't have the money right now, and it will be some time before I can return it all. Please wait a moment." The Rebbe left the room, returning a few minutes later with a pair of valuable silver candlesticks in his hands.

"These candlesticks are worth a lot of money. Take them as collateral, until I return the money that your wife gave me without your permission," he said, placing the candlesticks in the man's hands. The visitor stood, awestruck and astonished by the Rebbe's greatness, now so clearly revealed to him.

Silver candlesticks, in an era where a potato cut in half was considered a fine receptacle for candles, were no small matter. But the man did not refuse them, particularly in the face of the Rebbe's exhortations. "But be careful," the Rebbe warned him, wagging his finger, "don't let your wife know about this. Hide the candlesticks well, so that no one sees them!"

⌘

The valuable candlesticks were secreted in a hiding place all through the winter, until they were all but forgotten. But before Pesach all good Jewish women begin to poke into every crack and hole, and soon enough the candlesticks were discovered by the woman of the house. "Did you get some kind of inheritance?" she asked her husband, who began to stammer an incoherent explanation that did not satisfy her at all. She would not let up, asking him again and again, until all was revealed.

"They are the holy Rebbe's candlesticks!" she said furiously. "My money, that I merited to donate so that our names would be blessed, you want it back? And you dared take the candlesticks belonging to the Rebbe himself? The Rebbe offered them and so you, in your wisdom, agreed to take them?" she said scornfully. "Give them back immediately," she screamed at her dumbfounded husband.

The man rushed to the Rebbe's house and begged him to do him the favor and take back the candlesticks, as it was a matter of *shalom bayis*. Of course, he would forgo payment of the debt.

When the Rebbe saw what was happening, he said, "Do you have a grown-up girl in your house? I will suggest a proper match for her, the wonderful son of the rabbi of Vladimirch. I will not accept a matchmaker's fee; instead my debt to you will be canceled."

And the Rebbe immediately sat down and wrote to his *chassid*, the rabbi of Vladimirch, telling him to betroth his talented son to the lovely daughter of this man — and *mazel tov*, for she was intended for him from Heaven.

When the man returned to his home with the Rebbe's letter in hand, there was great rejoicing and happiness. A holiday atmosphere prevailed, and the man, thrown out so unceremoniously not long before, became the hero of the day, in the merit of the letter which he bore.

Immediately after Pesach the family took a carriage from Stolin to Vladimirch. The bride's brothers and sisters, too, joined the group, in anticipation of the upcoming event. Throughout the journey, the father held onto the Rebbe's letter as one clings to an object of great value. Every once in a while he would read its contents aloud, emphasizing those wonderful words, "...she is intended for him from Heaven."

"Nu, my daughter, we will arrive in Vladimirch as unknowns, but in a few days all will point you out as the rabbi's daughter-in-law," he said contentedly to his daughter. And she? Her eyes lit up with delight and happiness.

On their arrival in Vladimirch they hurried to the local inn to rest their weary bones. That evening they saw the innkeeper getting ready to leave, dressed in his Shabbos finery. It couldn't be a wedding — these were the days of *Sefiras HaOmer*, when marriages were forbidden.

"What holiday is it?" the family asked him. The innkeeper, for a moment forgetting that these people couldn't possibly know the local news, said impatiently, "Didn't you know? It's a holiday for the people of Vladimirch; tonight the son of our rabbi is becoming engaged to the daughter of one of the rich men of the town."

The family paled. The rabbi's son to marry one of the local girls — and not their daughter? But what of the Rebbe's promise?

The father jumped up from his place, grabbed the letter out of his pocket, and thrust it in his wife's face in a surge of fury.

"Here's the 'ruach hakodesh' of your Rebbe!" he said bitterly, with a laugh that was half a sob. "Run to your rebbes, give them a lot of money so that they can make fools of us."

The woman remained unmoved. Cooly, she bent down and picked up the forlorn piece of paper that had floated to the floor, without saying a word. When they returned home she hid the letter, occasionally reading it in private as tears flowed down her face.

Weeks, months, years passed. The holy Rebbe was called from this world to the next.

The father of the family repaired hats for a living. One day, a man whose dirty face and shabby clothing left no doubt that he was a lowly beggar, walked into the shop, a large box in his hand. From the box he pulled out a particularly beautiful *shtreimel*. "Do you want to buy a lovely *shtreimel* for a good price?" he asked.

The man's breath was taken away; he had never seen such a beautiful *shtreimel*. Certainly not in the hands of a beggar. "Where did you get such a thing?" he asked suspiciously.

"Oh, those were the days," the beggar sighed. "Once, I was rich..." In a quiet voice he told the man the story of his life. He had been a resident of the village of Vladimirch, a wealthy man who had actually had his daughter betrothed to the rabbi's wonderful son. He bought this beautiful *shtreimel* for his future son-in-law, but suddenly his life changed. He lost all his money, and the engagement was broken.

"Your daughter didn't marry the rabbi's son?" the man asked breathlessly.

"No," the beggar cried. "G-d's hand was upon me; my life has become so hard."

When the beggar finished his tale he was astonished to see that the man had disappeared. At that very moment the repairman was standing in his house. "Do you have the Rebbe's letter?" he demanded from his wife.

"What's happened?" The woman was confused.

He told her all about the beggar. The woman went to her hiding place and pulled out the forgotten letter.

The next day the hat repairman and his wife and daughter traveled to Vladimirch. This time they were absolutely certain — The man accepted his wife's endless rebuke with good grace. "Okay, I didn't have enough faith in the great man. A *tzaddik's* words come true, even if there are obstacles in the way," he admitted.

The letter, brought a few years late, worked its magic and the match was made. At the wedding, the bridegroom wore a particularly beautiful *shtreimel*.

And the Rebbe's words, "She is intended for him from Heaven," were fulfilled.

A Gift with Dignity

R' FEITEL, A TEACHER IN THE TOWN OF YASI, WAS A PAUPER. Not a mere pauper: R' Feitel knew the misery of the most degrading form of poverty.

He had seven daughters, and nothing else, not even bread. In the morning they did not know what they would eat that night; that night, if luck had sent them a bit to eat, they again did not know what would stay the pangs of hunger the next morning. It hardly needs stating that the family members were all clothed in rags.

As we have said, R' Feitel was a teacher of young students, and an excellent one at that. But ability is one thing and remuneration for it quite another. Almost all the parents were paupers themselves and they could hardly find a few pennies to give to their children to hand to their faithful teacher every month.

And so the years passed. R' Feitel continued to teach the little ones with reverence and love for G-d, with devotion and joy. He never gave a thought to life's necessities, and saw the meager salary as incidental. More years should have flown by in the same manner, with R' Feitel satisfied with his lot and never complaining about his poverty. However, one day R' Shmuel, the rav of Yasi, woke up.

The messenger who tapped on R' Feitel's door was shocked by the squalor before him when he opened the battered door on its creaking hinges and saw what lay behind it. R' Feitel's poverty was no secret in the town of Yasi, and most of the residents lived in uncertain economic conditions, a group of beggars together. And yet, it seemed to this messenger that the poverty that he was viewing here was unlike all others. He had seen poor men's homes before, but never before had he looked upon such a hovel, a home lacking in everything. His searching eyes did not fall on even one chair in the gloom, and he surmised that the heap of straw in the middle of the floor served that purpose. There was no table worthy of the name in the room either; a few boards lying shakily on rocks were a poor substitute.

He stood still for a few moments, until he found his tongue. "The Rav, R' Shmuel, may he live and be well, has asked that you come to his house as soon as possible."

R' Shmuel, rav and head of Yasi's *beis din*, was a notable scholar and pious man, possessing a kind and warm manner of speech. R' Feitel's miserable condition had not escaped his notice, but until today he had not known how to rescue him from his dire situation. At last he had found a solution.

"How are you, R' Feitel?" asked the Rav with more than a trace of love and warmth in his voice.

"Thank G-d we have bread to eat and clothes to wear," R' Feitel answered bashfully.

"And your daughters? What will be of them?" The Rav's words pierced R' Feitel's heart. "Not only do I not accept your statement regarding bread and clothing — from all I've heard they are far from satisfactory — but your daughters are growing up quickly. How will you marry them off? What dowry can you give?"

R' Feitel was silent: The question was a tough one. In truth, he had been, in the secret recesses of his mind and heart, mulling over the problem for a long time, but since the time for marriage had not arrived he had not taken any action. Why bother today with tomorrow's worries?

R' Shmuel lashed out at him. "Even if you bury your head in the sand, won't time pass anyway? Soon the matchmakers will be knocking at your door, but they'll disappear as quickly as they came. Will you be able to bring in-laws in to visit your home? Not to mention that you haven't even a penny for a dowry!"

"I thought that perhaps I would tutor less gifted children at night, and so be able to save a few *groschen*," R' Feitel stammered.

"*Nu*, R' Feitel, be honest, from a few miserable coins you'll be able to marry off seven daughters?"

R' Feitel again remained silent. He could not imagine what the rabbi wanted of him. He understood that he was trying to tell him something, but what could it be?

"Listen to me, R' Feitel," the Rav said after a short moment of quiet. "A Jew like you, with seven daughters to marry off, has to think ahead. Even if Korach opens his treasure house for you, you still won't have enough."

"I don't understand," R' Feitel said, with just a flicker of impatience in his voice.

"I'm trying to tell you that your daughters' future is not just a matter of money," the Rav explained patiently. "You have to stop being Feitel the wretched pauper and go out and get yourself the reputation of a respected man of means. If you don't, who'll want to make a match with you? I'm sure you want to marry your daughters off to scholars, don't you?

"And so, R' Feitel, you've got to make yourself into a respected and prosperous man. That's the simple truth," the Rav finished succinctly.

R' Feitel was completely confused. Was the Rav teasing him?

"No, no," R' Shmuel finally said. "Heaven forbid. I honestly and truly mean to change your position!"

And then the Rav revealed his secret. He was planning on moving soon to *Eretz Yisrael*, to live in the city of Tzefas, and so he was asking R' Feitel to leave his hovel and live in the Rav's large house, which included several apartments. R' Feitel could rent out the apartments and from the rental fees he would be able to save enough to marry his daughters off respectably!

R' Feitel wondered if his ears were playing tricks on him. "The Rav is giving me his house as a gift?"

"Did you hear me mention a gift?" the Rav laughed. "I'm not crazy. Who would give such a thing away? The house is worth at least one hundred *rendlich*."

"If so, how will I pay for it?" R' Feitel asked the inevitable question. "Only a rich man could buy such a large house; the Rav himself inherited it from his father-in-law, who was a very prosperous man."

"You'll pay in installments," the Rav explained, pulling out a detailed agreement. He asked R' Feitel to sit with him at his desk and go over the contract paragraph by paragraph, to ensure that all was written in accordance with the laws set out in the *Shulchan Aruch*.

R' Feitel took the contract with him. He walked through the streets of Yasi as if in a dream. Such a turn of events! Who would have imagined it? And yet he was afraid. The terms of the contract seemed too difficult to fulfill. R' Shmuel had no need for legal advice in order to protect his interests, the Rav himself was an expert in business law as set forth in the *Choshen Mishpat* section of the *Shulchan Aruch*, and he had inserted detail after detail in order to protect himself. He included the following terms: R' Feitel was to send him a monthly allotment of a *rendel* for the next eight years. After all, R' Shmuel did not know how he would be making a living in *Eretz Yisrael*. He was no longer young, and did not have the energy to start looking for new jobs now. A *rendel* was about the average monthly wage of a rabbi in a medium-sized congregation. If, for whatever reason, R' Feitel would miss a payment, even by a short time, the entire agreement would be null and void!

"You're not sure what you should tell R' Shmuel?" R' Feitel's wife asked in surprise. "Our rabbi, in his goodness, is handing you salvation on a silver platter and you're hesitating?"

"But where will we get a *rendel* to send him every month to Tzefas?" R' Feitel asked in despair.

"We'll save it from our own bread," his wife said proudly. "And we'll be able to marry off our children to great scholars."

R' Feitel did not waste any more time: He agreed to the rabbi's terms and in a few weeks R' Feitel's friends and acquaintances watched, openmouthed, as he left his miserable dwelling for the spacious, former home of the Rav, who had already left for *Eretz Yisrael*.

R' Feitel thus became, to all appearances, a respected man of means in his city. He rented out all the empty apartments in his new home; he himself took up residence in the Rav's home. With all this, he did not miss one day of teaching.

Everyone believed that R' Feitel had, in one day, turned into a wealthy man. It did not take long for the matchmakers to come knocking. R' Feitel married off three of his daughters, one after the other, to the best scholars of the region, and saw to it that each received a fine dowry.

Everything was lovely, it seemed. But appearance is not always reality. No one knew that R' Feitel and his family were still living the same life of want and hunger, there in their beautiful home. The rental fees that R' Feitel collected were all used for dowries. He saved up that monthly rendel that he was to send to *Eretz Yisrael* from out of his meager earnings, collecting penny after penny from out of the mouths of his family.

Three years passed, and R' Feitel felt that he was cracking under the strain. And then came the first month when he did not have a *rendel* to send. The next month he worked twice as hard and somehow managed to wrest the money out of his mouth and send it on. But then came another month when he could not find the cash.

In short, after some last, futile efforts R' Feitel stopped sending money to Tzefas, waiting for the missive that would announce that the contract was terminated, as had been agreed upon.

But there was no response at all.

The news of the death of R' Shmuel, former rabbi of Yasi, reached the town from Tzefas just eight years after his move to the holy land. His three sons, who served as rabbis in important congregations in Rumania and Galicia, began a correspondence with the notables of Tzefas, who sent them R' Shmuel's last will and testament, as well as a large number of private business papers. The sons looked through the contracts and learned that R' Feitel had bought the large house in Yasi from their father. But he had failed to fulfill the terms of the contract, having sent the *rendel* to Tzefas for just over three years.

The contract was null and void!

The three sons called R' Feitel to a *din Torah*. R' Feitel prepared to fight for his life.

"You cheated our father for five years and didn't send him what you owed him. Who knows if he had anything to eat during those years?" the sons said. "We'll forgive that; what's done is done. But our father, may he rest in peace, specifically wrote that if you missed even one payment, the contract was nullified."

On the other side stood R' Feitel, woefully telling how he and his family had starved themselves for three full years, sending the payments faithfully, until their strength had given out.

The judges were perplexed. On the one hand it seemed that the sons of the rabbi of Yasi were correct. And yet, how could they throw an entire family out onto the streets, and take a Jew away from his source of income at a time when he still had four daughters to marry off? They took their problem to another *beis din*, but this one, too, gave up on the problem. Rabbinic judges in Poland, Galicia, Rumania, and Hungary pondered the case; great Torah scholars were called upon to give their opinions, rabbis discussed it in the *beis midrash*. Torah Jewry was in an uproar.

In his distress, R' Feitel traveled to his rabbi, R' Yechezkel of Shiniva, to pour his heart out. His rabbi told him, "Go travel to Gorlitz, to my brother R' Baruch, who is known as an expert in solving such dilemmas. Otherwise, you're certain to lose the case."

"What makes him so powerful?" R' Feitel asked.

"He's the only one who can help you," R' Yechezkel replied. "He's brave as a leopard and strong as a lion, and in cases where everyone else was ready to surrender he managed to win. Even the heavenly court accepts his judgment. There was once a Jew who felt unbelievable pains in his stomach. It seemed that he'd been stricken with a terrible disease, and all the doctors had given up on him. The man traveled to Berlin, where surgeons opened his stomach and saw that the disease had spread throughout his body. There was nothing to be done, they said, wishing him farewell and Godspeed.

"The man returned to his house and burst out crying. Who wants to die, after all? He went from *tzaddik* to *tzaddik* until he reached me. I immediately sent him on to Gorlitz."

"And what did R' Baruch tell him?" R' Feitel's curiosity had been aroused.

"He promised that if he brought him 300 rendels, his cure was certain.

"The sick man returned to his city. The people went wild: They ran to and fro selling their valuables and jewelry, for the man was much beloved by all.

"One of the man's relatives, who was also close to the Rebbe of Gorlitz, traveled to the *tzaddik*.

"'Why has my friend come to my house?' the Rebbe asked him. The man said he had just been passing by, but that did not fool the Rebbe; he was too clever for that. He turned his wise eyes upon him and said, 'No one comes to Gorlitz just for a visit. What's on your mind? Speak.'

"'Can it be?' the sick man's relative asked. 'You promise a cure to one who is terminally ill? And not only that, but you ask for a fortune, 300 *rendels*? To fleece the entire village?'

"'I knew you didn't like me, but I didn't realize just how much,' the Rebbe shouted at him, but there was a smile on his face. 'For once I can get hold of 300 *rendels*, and you're taking away my income? Let him come here with the money and he will leave here a healthy man,' he concluded firmly.

"And so it was. The money was brought to R' Baruch — who promptly dispersed it among the poor — and the dying man stood up and lived!"

Without further delay, R' Feitel traveled to Gorlitz. When he reached the city he poured out his woes to R' Baruch. R' Baruch was less impressed with the tears than he was with the obvious honesty that lay behind them, and he ordered his assistant, "In another month the annual fair takes place. As you know, during that time the government discounts train travel, in order to encourage the public to attend the fair. Write letters to the three sons of the deceased former rabbi of Yasi asking them to come to me then for a *din Torah*."

On the appointed day the three brothers, all of them rabbis, stood in the home of the Rebbe of Gorlitz, R' Feitel standing across from them. The Rebbe heard out both sides carefully. In the heat of the debate he held up his hand and said loudly, "Enough! I've heard enough!"

And to the astonishment of all the participants, R' Baruch stood up in a boiling rage, pulled off his *tzitzis* and pushed his white shirt to the side, until his chest was bare.

"The *Shach* and the *Sma*, those great halachic commentators, are found in here!" he cried, pointing at his chest. "I don't have to be taught what is written within them. I have learned more than a little *Shulchan Aruch* too," he thundered, his voice echoing through the room, "and I tell you," he turned to the three brothers with great severity, "your late father knew perfectly well that R' Feitel could not keep his obligations up forever, and he had no intention of his doing so. He wanted to give the gift and let him keep his dignity, as a partner in business and not as a beggar. The thing that you are asking for is nothing more than theft! Absolute theft!"

The three heirs of the rabbi of Yasi immediately announced that they absolved all claims against R' Feitel.

The news of the judgment reached the *tzaddik* R' Yechezkel of Shiniva, R' Baruch of Gorlitz's older brother. In response he said, "It's just as I said. Only my brother could make such a judgment, in the deepest spirit of the simplicity of the Torah."

A Watery Grave

THAT NIGHT RESEMBLED THE NIGHTS THAT PRECEDED AND those that followed it. It was a normal Jerusalem evening. The sky stretched over the city like velvet beaded with the twinkling of thousands of stars. A round midmonth full moon promenaded above, flooding the scenery with its pure white glow.

The city was bathed in the night's stillness. Even late revelers were in their beds for a few snatches of sleep, while the early risers had not yet awoken. Thus the streets were deserted.

A figure in dark clothing walked on the road that led from the city to the Shiloach spring. This was nothing remarkable: Every night R' Yitzchak Dovid Grossman would go down to immerse himself in the *mikveh* of the Shiloach, popularly known as the *mikveh* of R' Yishmael the High Priest. It is said that R' Yishmael used to immerse himself in it prior to his Temple duties.

Jerusalem residents appreciated the uniqueness of the *mikveh* of the Shiloach. For one thing, it certainly could boast of many illustrious forebears. What's more, the *mikveh* was carved out of the mountain at the very opening of the Shiloach spring. As a result, its waters were always clean and pure. Residents of Jerusalem — a city not blessed with large amounts of water — knew that the water of most *mikvehs* was changed once every six months. Thus they valued a *mikveh* that contained sparkling, fresh water.

A final point: Where else could one find a mikveh open at 1 o'clock in the morning?

Perhaps you will ask, who is forcing R' Yitzchak Dovid to go to the Silwan valley, on the steeply sloping downward path with its strange undergrowth, a path that became even more treacherous and difficult on the return journey? Why could he not merely wait for dawn and join the others who prayed at sunrise in their immersion in the *mikveh* at the Churvah shul?

Had you asked R' Yitzchak Dovid himself, he undoubtedly would have looked at you as if you did not know what you were talking about. This nocturnal immersion was simply the preparation for the learning of the Torah's deepest secrets, the mysteries set forth in the holy *Zohar*.

This study had many merits. First, learning in the *Zohar* led to purity of the soul, as everyone knew. Second, the air at this hour was pure; the rule of the powers of impurity that came forth with dusk eased at midnight, thus making these hours particularly propitious for esoteric learning.

The third merit? His *chavrusa*.

For R' Yitzchak Dovid had merited what few had ever experienced. He learned with R' Duvid'l.

R' Dovid, known fondly by Jerusalemites as Reb Duvid'l, was beloved and admired by all. The men and women of Jerusalem did nothing without consulting him. When he would walk through the market of the Old City everyone would clear the way before his shining countenance. Even the Arab stall owners would stand up in reverence before the "*chakim al Yahud, chakim Daoud.*"

R' Duvid'l was a man of great stature, yet he behaved with admirable simplicity, walking through the streets like one of the common people. In his modesty he did not allow others to view him during his studies. Whatever he learned he learned privately, quietly. One hardly ever saw him learning publicly. Few knew when he was learning; fewer, still, actually merited learning with him.

One of those chosen few was R' Yitzchak Dovid Grossman. R' Yitzchak Dovid was one of the most able scholars in the holy city and one of the most pious among the *chassidim* of Karlin. He was a monumental student of the hidden Torah. Few knew his secret, why he merited such unusual talent: He was R' Duvid'l's study partner in Kabbalah.

Every night after midnight, R' Duvid'l and R' Yitzchak Dovid would find a hidden corner and delve into the *Zohar*, the writings of the Ari HaKadosh, and R' Chaim Vital, until dawn.

R' Yitzchak Dovid, in his desire to purify himself before such study, would go down to the valley every night, to the Shiloach spring on the edge of the Arab village of Silwan, and immerse himself in the *mikveh* of R' Yishmael the High Priest. Then, in perfect purity of body and soul, he and his illustrious *chavrusa* would study the secrets of Torah.

And so it continued, for many years.

That night resembled the nights that preceded and followed it. And yet in one way it was entirely different: in the violence that was to take place during those dark hours.

When R' Yitzchak Dovid descended the winding path down the mountain no one could see him. Of that he was certain. It was better for him to go to immersion without the eyes of his people upon him — and without the eyes of those who were not of his people. His people? Because of his humility, R' Yitzchak Dovid didn't want to reveal the secret he shared with R' Duvid'l. That was all he needed: To have others point at him and say, "Here is the kabbalist, R' Duvid'l's *chavrusa*."

And those who were not his people? That was because of the danger involved. Every night he placed his head into the lion's mouth, as he descended into a village brimming with bloodthirsty Arabs whose hatred against all that was Jewish was monumental. Woe to him, should any of those thugs happen ever upon him.

And so he snuck down, wearing cloth shoes that would make no noise. He entered the *mikveh* hastily and even more hastily immersed. The entire procedure took no more than a few minutes and he was already climbing back up towards the city.

R' Yitzchak was certain that no one could see him — but he was sorely mistaken. On his way to the spring on this night he did not notice the shadowy figure hugging the walls of the homes, following him on tiptoe.

This was one of the neighbors, a young Arab ruffian whose thoughts were full of violence. One warm night he could not sleep and in the darkness he had heard sounds in the *mikveh*. Stealthily he had gone out to see what was happening there. The next night he did the same thing.

"Oh, a Jew comes by himself every night at the same time!" he discovered. His wicked brain came up with a satanic scheme. And on this night he made plans to carry it out.

R' Yitzchak Dovid removed his clothing and lay them on a nearby stone. Another minute and he was in the water. He bent his head and went underwater.

He went under — and did not come up. At the moment that R' Yitzchak Dovid had put his head under the purifying waters, the Arab had jumped out with lightning speed and placed his burly hands on the Jew's head.

R' Yitzchak Dovid, horrified, felt his breath running out. He tried to pull his head away from those pincerlike hands, he moved his body to and fro, to no avail.

"I shouldn't have endangered myself; the Arab is trying to kill me," he thought in despair. With the last of his strength he tried to struggle, jumping and writhing, contorting like a snake beneath those merciless arms. But all his attempts to escape were in vain: He was trapped beneath the water and on the verge of a terrible death.

His lungs burned. He longed for just one breath of air, a breath that would restore life to his suffocating body before he exploded. His thoughts grew fuzzy. He tried desperately to remember the words of *Viduy*, but who could confess his sins when his entire body was being tortured?

Suddenly there was the sound of racing footsteps. The *mikveh's* door burst open noisily and R' Duvid'l flew in like a stormy gust of wind. In his hurry R' Duvid'l had not found the time to put on his hat and golden-striped Yerushalmi kaftan; he had raced to the *mikveh* in his white *yarmulke* and *tzitzis*. In the blink of an eye he was on the crouching figure of the Arab, pounding hammer blows with a mighty fist.

The Arab lay on the floor, lifeless and inert.

R' Yitzchak Dovid felt that his time was at hand; thousands of white-hot needles stabbed his agonized lungs. And, just as suddenly as it had begun, it was gone: The terrible pressure disappeared from his head. He jumped up in the water and took a deep, satisfying breath.

R' Duvid'l helped him out of the water. It took some time for him to recover completely from the ordeal.

"What happened?" R' Yitzchak Dovid asked, pointing to the corpse, speaking with difficulty. His entire body was still shaking.

R' Duvid'l smiled. "I gave him what he deserved," he said. "We won't see him again, even when the dead are resurrected."

As time passed, R' Yitzchak Dovid began to comprehend the enormity of the miracle. With tears in his eyes he thanked his benefactor profusely. "You saved me from certain death."

He paused, "How did you know to come just at that moment?" he asked R' Duvid'l. "One minute later and I would have been in another world. I don't understand at all," he added, after a moment's thought. "How did you know that I was here and in mortal danger?"

R' Duvid'l, in characteristic modesty, took care of the matter with one offhand sentence.

"My heart told me my good friend was in trouble."

"But how did R' Duvid'l know where his good friend was?" R' Yitzchak Dovid's friends in the *beis midrash* of Stolin were adamant in their questions, after they heard of the miracle that had been performed for him, and after he finished saying the blessing "*HaGomel.*"

"And is that the only thing that's hard to understand?" one of the elder *chassidim* said. "In my opinion the entire matter is incredible. How long can a person be without air? Some say two minutes, others three. Yet the road from R' Duvid'l's home to the Silwan, even if taken running, is 10 minutes. So figure out, how much time passed from the moment the cruel Arab tried to drown R' Yitzchak Dovid, to the time R' Duvid'l arrived?"

"What do you mean?" one of the *chassidim* asked.

"Choose one," the elderly *chassid* replied. "Either R' Duvid'l managed to get to the *mikveh* like one who can fly, or he began his mad dash to the Shiloach even before the incident had begun! Either way," the *chassid* ended, "it doesn't really matter. Whatever happened, it certainly can only be explained as a miracle."

Measure for Measure, Twice Over

IN THE KOLLEL OFFICE IN JERUSALEM THE TELEPHONE, a square wooden box with a cumbersome receiver lying on top, sounded its shrill ring.

A telephone was a rare and exciting piece of equipment in the Jerusalem of 80 years ago. The era of telecommunications itself was still new, and the miraculous device known as a "*sach-rachok*" was available only to large institutions or corporations that managed to get hold of one: influential companies, hospitals, army bases, and important offices such as this one — the office of Kollel Galicia.

R' Chaim K. picked up the receiver and listened. After a minute passed he replaced the receiver and put on his overcoat and hat.

"The Turk called me," he told his secretary, R' Shmuel Aharon, as he buttoned his coat and smoothed down his beard. "I wonder what he wants."

"What Turk is that?" R' Shmuel Aharon asked.

"The head of the military base for the Jerusalem area," R' Chaim sighed. "What can he want, more names of *kollel* students who've avoided the draft?" He pulled out a thin gold chain and stared at the watch attached to it. "It's 12:30 now. I assume I'll be back in about an hour. Please finish translating the letters."

He left the room, and the secretary continued his work. In old Jerusalem a working knowledge of German was a valuable asset, and R' Shmuel Aharon excelled in translation both from and into that language. It was this ability that had landed him the job of secretary of the large *kollel*.

After more than an hour had elapsed, R' Chaim returned, upset and bewildered.

"What did the commander want?" the secretary asked hesitantly.

"Very strange. He asked that within 48 hours I give him a list of all the members of my entire family living here, from me down to my youngest grandchild."

There was an overtone of anger in his voice. It was to be expected: Eighty years ago one who was in charge of a large Jerusalem *kollel* had enormous authority and an almost royal position. One word of his could determine the fate of a *kollel* student, for good or for ill. With the nod of his head he decided the amount of the monthly stipend, the place where the student would live, whether a young married man was entitled to receive a special Pesach subsidy. Now R' Chaim felt somehow degraded. The request for him to prepare a list of his family members smacked of disrespect for his lofty position.

R' Shmuel Aharon wrinkled his brow. Why would the military commander need a list of R' Chaim's family? Neither man could come up with a reason for the strange request. R' Chaim sat at his desk and began to pen the requested list: the names of his sons and daughters, his sons-in-law and daughters-in-law, his grandsons and granddaughters. Only his son Gad was omitted, for Gad lived in Holland.

Two days later R' Chaim went to the local base and handed in the list: 28 names in all.

On Rosh Chodesh Nisan the telephone in the *kollel* office rang once again.

R' Chaim impatiently grabbed the receiver and listened, his face growing ashen.

"What's happened?" his secretary asked, concerned.

R' Chaim was in shock. "The commander has summoned me to appear before him. This was no request; it was an order."

"If so, I'm coming with you," the faithful secretary said. The two were soon walking through the courtyard of the *kollel*, and then stepping through the streets of new Jerusalem towards the Damascus Gate, where the Turkish regional commander maintained his headquarters. Jerusalemites used to tremble in fear and disgust when forced to pass that way. Fear, before the Turkish command; disgust, because they were headquartered in a Franciscan church.

On their way they tried to guess what the commander wanted. R' Chaim was certain that behind all the excitement lurked a desire to bring him down a bit, to show him that despite his exalted position he was not all powerful: There were those who were more powerful and who ranked above him!

When they reached the commander's office they separated; R' Chaim entered and his secretary waited for him outside, wondering very much what the mystery was.

He did not have to wait very long to find out.

After a few minutes R' Chaim K. walked out, his face scarlet with anger and humiliation. "Would you believe it? A command of exile!" He waved a piece of paper before the secretary's astonished face, his voice choked with emotion.

"Exile?" The secretary stammered. "Whom are they exiling?"

"Me! The executive almost broke out in tears. "They want to exile me and my family. And when? In exactly 14 days! *Erev Pesach*, my family and I must leave Jerusalem and travel to Askashir!"

R' Shmuel Aharon read the decree of exile that was signed by the Turkish high commander, Jamal Pasha himself. "The members of the K. family," it stated, "men, women, and children, from the eldest to the youngest, must leave Jerusalem and travel to Askashir in 14 days."

"But why?" R' Shmuel Aharon tried to understand it. "What did you do? What are you accused of?"

The executive flared up. "I don't know anything more than you do! They wouldn't give me another detail. 'This is your decree of exile. Now get out of here.' That is the sum total of what the commander told me."

"Oh, it's no big deal." The secretary waved off the entire affair with a shake of his hand. "Nothing will come of it; it will never be enacted."

"And on whose authority do you have this?" R' Chaim asked bitterly.

"You're an Austrian subject," the secretary explained. "We'll go directly to the Austrian Consulate, speak with the consul, and have this capricious decree annulled. The world is not completely lawless."

R' Chaim heaved a sigh of relief. "You're right. I was so upset and angry, I wasn't thinking. Yes, absolutely, the consul, Mr. Friedrich Krautz, is my close friend, and is truly good to the Jews. He'll never allow this."

They immediately made their way to the Austrian Consulate. The consul reacted as expected: His face grew red with anger and he slammed his fist onto his desk with such force that the room shook. "Jamal Pasha thinks he's got Jerusalem in his pocket? I'll show him! The kingdom of Austria will not allow one of its citizens to be exiled from Palestine for no reason."

The consul promised R' Chaim that he would have an audience with Jamal Pasha in the coming days. R' Chaim, his concerns eased, returned to his home. A consul in Ottoman Palestine had the status of a ruler; the Austrian consul, particularly, was a strong and respected figure. R' Shmuel Aharon felt that R' Chaim could already drink a *l'chayim* to celebrate the decree's annulment.

Later that day, R' Shmuel Aharon went to the home of R' Duvid'l Biderman, the Rebbe of Lelov, who was considered by many the unofficial leader of the Jews of Jerusalem. He told him what had happened, describing it as if it were yesterday's news, certain that the Rebbe would shrug it off. After all, the Austrian consul himself was getting involved!

To his great surprise and consternation, the Rebbe reacted very differently. R' Shmuel Aharon's observant eyes did not miss the strange trembling that overcame the Rebbe when he heard of the decree of exile. It was a short shudder, hardly noticeable, but the perceptive and wise *chassid* saw it and recognized it for what it was: The Rebbe was terrified! The Rebbe asked for details of the matter, his voice not revealing a thing, but his gestures telling of deep concerns behind the news. The Rebbe, at least, seemed to accept the decree as fact. In his eyes, the executive had already been banished.

And yet R' Shmuel Aharon himself was convinced of R' Chaim's absolute, unquestioned authority. No one had ever dared disagree with him until now; surely he would not be exiled. He also put great hopes in the upcoming meeting between the consul and Jamal Pasha. And so he saw the decree as a bitter pill, but one that could yet be easily sweetened.

The consul, as promised, went to Jamal Pasha, but his confidence was shattered in the ruler's office. Pasha was adamant, and turned harshly upon the Austrian consul for having the temerity to interfere in a purely Turkish domestic matter.

The consul didn't give up; he telegraphed the Austrian palace, and brought other consuls into the fray. But all was for naught. The Turkish ruler was firm: R' Chaim and his family would leave Jerusalem on *erev Pesach*!

R' Chaim didn't raise his hands in surrender either. He turned to rabbis, to business leaders, to well-known public figures. Each one did what he could. Delegations raced here and there. Jamal Pasha agreed to see high-placed envoys, one after the other. He answered all with a resounding negative. Finally, he revealed the reason behind the banishment.

R' Chaim's son, R' Gad, lived in Holland, a country that had carefully kept its neutrality in the terrible world war that was being fought all through Europe. That winter, in the year 5677 (1917), a time when the lifeblood of the Turkish Empire was being drained in its battle with England, R' Gad had written to his father in Jerusalem:

"In the matter of the world war that is continuing, and that has created such a difficult situation: Don't worry. The defeated Turks are keeping the truth from you, and acting as if their sovereignty over you is eternal. But we in the free world know the truth: The British are on the verge of victory. They will soon conquer Palestine and put an end to the Ottoman rule. The hunger will cease, the plagues and the scarcity will end. Salvation is near."

The letter never reached R' Chaim. On its way to Palestine it passed through Istanbul and fell into the hands of the German censor there. The Turks and the Germans were allies in this war, and the letter was brought to the attention of the Turkish regime. It was investigated, and a finger was pointed at the father of the letter's author. Nothing else was needed. Such a letter, penned during wartime! "A spy!" fumed the Germans. "Such clear information to reach Palestine and cause a terrible breach of morale among the Turkish troops?"

And so it seemed that it was the Germans, not the Turks, who were behind the decree of exile. The great Jamal Pasha was no more than a cog in a huge war machine.

Now the executive understood the command to prepare a list of his family members. "And I wrote them all down; I fell into the trap like a complete fool," his conscience bit at him. "If I had left out a few names, the Turks would never have known."

But what was done could not be undone.

In the meantime the news was out in Jerusalem, and the city was abuzz.

"From one letter?" Everyone trembled when they heard the dreadful news of the cruel decree. "Men of such stature in the community to be exiled from the city? And for what? And the despots could not find a different day to do it than the day before Pesach?"

Younger members of the community tried to find out information about the unknown city of Askashir. What they found filled them with dread: The city of Askashir was located in Asiatic Turkey, in the heart of a forlorn and wild area, remote from any civilization.

When R' Chaim realized that he was to be banished into the outer darkness, a terrible fear overcame him. Slowly the scope of the tragedy became clear. All the delegations, all the community representatives, charged into a brick wall. Jamal Pasha was determined to banish R' Chaim and his family, no matter what.

In great distress, R' Shmuel Aharon brought R' Chaim's plight to the attention of his Rebbe, R' Duvid'l.

Much to his shock, R' Duvid'l acted as though the sorrow of R' Chaim did not disturb him in the least.

R' Shmuel Aharon persisted. He knew that his Rebbe's warm heart was no doubt bleeding over the plight of the man. Perhaps he wanted R' Chaim to grow even more fervent in his prayers. But the days went by, *erev Pesach* was approaching — and with it the banishment of 28 innocent people.

He returned to his Rebbe, who loved the Jews with such fervor that the people of Jerusalem saw in him not a holy Rebbe but a merciful mother completely caught up in his people's troubles. But, to his consternation and amazement, the Rebbe absolutely refused to get involved, behaving with severe coolness when told of the plight of the unfortunate R' Chaim and his family. With a gesture of acceptance, the Rebbe sent his *chassid* away, as if the decree were final and nothing further could be done.

When R' Chaim saw his options disappearing, he took a flask of olive oil and went with it to the holy Rebbe. In Jerusalem it was well known that in times of trouble one took such a flask to the Rebbe, at his request, and all problems were resolved. The sick grew well, money troubles disappeared, Arab enemies died — all after R' Duvid'l rolled a wick and lit a candle from the flask brought to him.

R' Duvid'l would speak to his *chassidim* every day between *Minchah* and *Maariv*, telling them tales of great men. Those in the know claimed that there was no better time than this to approach

R' Duvid'l, as he told tales of miracles from days gone by — for he would then attempt to continue those miracles and bring their influence into the present day.

R' Chaim entered the *beis midrash* and approached the Rebbe, courteously and with submission. This, obviously, was not the same stern and proud executive whom all of Jerusalem feared. His knees trembled and his eyes gave off glints of fear.

"Would the Rebbe light from the oil that I've brought?" he asked in a low voice.

R' Duvid'l took the flask from him, his face motionless.

Wise *chassidim* realized immediately that this flask would not effect a redemption. First, R' Chaim had brought it without having been asked by the Rebbe. Second, now that it had been brought, the Rebbe did not show a single sign of satisfaction or pleasure. He took the oil but made no promises.

On *erev Pesach* many in the city rose for sunrise prayers so that they would have enough time to eat a bit of *chametz* before it became forbidden and would have to be burned. But when they went out into the street, they saw a terrifying sight: A division of armed Turkish soldiers had encircled the area around the large Tiferes Yisrael Shul, known as Nisan Bak's *shul* in honor of its well-known founder. The soldiers were encamped before the home of the *kollel* executive, R' Chaim, to ensure that no one left it. The family members were taken out, one by one. The soldiers stood, a neat list in their hands, calling out names, making certain that no one was missing.

The screams and cries shattered the morning quiet, and the hearts of the onlookers — but not the hearts of the merciless Turks. They placed the entire family onto wagons, allowing them to take along only one bag each.

There was a terrible outcry in the city. The Turks had promised — and they had fulfilled their promise! They were banishing R' Chaim and his family, 28 people, without mercy. The Jerusalemites watched, objected, screamed, begged, pleaded, attempted bribery.

The soldiers seemed not to hear a word. Their ears, their hearts, were sealed, they did not answer and did not argue; grimly and quietly they did what they had set out to do.

R' Shmuel Aharon dashed to his Rebbe, crying stormily, "Help them! R' Chaim and his family are being taken away!"

The Rebbe shrugged his shoulders, as if to say, "The thing is done. What would you have me do?"

At noon R' Chaim and his entire family were placed aboard a train. *Seder* night was unceremoniously spent there. From the train they were taken to a ship, and after a few weeks they reached far-away Askashir. There they were placed in ramshackle huts, in a wild and uncivilized area that seemed to have been forgotten by man.

Jerusalem recognized R' Shmuel Aharon as a strong and stern man, possessed of a steel-tempered personality, one not apt to show his emotions. And yet, on *Seder* night he sat in his father R' Ben-Tziyon's home like a mourner at a wedding, occasionally breaking out in bitter sobs. R' Chaim had been his good friend, and the terrible image of his banishment haunted him in the midst of his four cups and three matzahs. He cried so that his father lashed out at him, "Stop that crying! You're ruining the holiday for the entire family!"

After a few weeks, postcards began arriving in Jerusalem from Askashir, postcards written in tears. R' Chaim and his family spoke of the bitterness of their lot, the humiliation of starvation, the terrible weather conditions, the life too hard to bear — Exile!

R' Shmuel Aharon took the postcards with him to his Rebbe's home. R' Duvid'l read the words written in blood and tears, his heart secretly breaking, his eyes moist. And yet, again, he turned to R' Shmuel Aharon and shrugged his shoulders, as one who has accepted the decree.

Finally, R' Shmuel Aharon's patience wore out. When a postcard whose words were a scream of horror arrived, he went to his Rebbe and lamented, "Why? Why such a terrible decree?"

The Rebbe gave him a stern glance, pondered for a while, and finally said, "Okay, now I can tell you. I see that you've forgotten, so I will remind you."

He was talking in riddles; R' Shmuel Aharon had no idea of what he meant.

"Do you remember So-and-So, that lonely person who died a year ago?" R' Duvid'l asked.

R' Shmuel Aharon sat up with a start. Of course he remembered. Who could forget?

A year before, a poor and solitary Jew had died in Jerusalem. He came from Galicia, and had died penniless. There was no one to pay for the burial expenses, for the *chevrah kaddisha*, the plot, the shrouds, and candles. Nothing!

In Jerusalem they always took great care that the body did not remain overnight without burial. Yet here was the dead man without anyone to take care, waiting two days, three, unburied. The *chevrah kaddisha* said that without payment they would not do their part.

The man's neighbors ran to the *kollel* and said, "The dead man belonged to you. You bury him."

But the *kollel* management answered, "The expenses are far too high. We can't do it all by ourselves, without help from anyone else."

R' Duvid'l himself belonged to Kollel Poland, but when he heard of the dead man rotting in his home, he could not ignore the shame. Like a tempest he flew to the home of R' Chaim and begged him, "*Gevald!* A humiliation for the dead man! How can you let that poor body rot in its home because of a question of money? For G-d's sake, bury him!"

R' Shmuel Aharon had been with the Rebbe during his race to R' Chaim's home, and he had heard with his own ears the terrible reply: "Don't get involved in our affairs. This is an internal question. Look, R' So-and-So got involved in our business, and he was thrown out of Jerusalem, all the way to America! And another one also got involved in our affairs, and he was sent as far as Cracow!"

The answer was a gross and brazen one, particularly since the man sent to America had been sent there by R' Duvid'l himself, while the other was also close to the Rebbe — and the *kollel* executive knew this very well.

"So now you understand," the Rebbe concluded. "He shouldn't have said that to me."

Now it was clear to R' Shmuel Aharon why the Rebbe had been so frightened at the news of the decree. He had immediately gotten to the heart of the matter and he knew that, despite his own desires, Heaven had taken offense at the Rebbe's dishonor and R' Chaim was fated to be exiled. Measure for measure.

R' Duvid'l had trembled and paled as he realized, with alarming swiftness, that the executive would pay a high price for having mocked a *tzaddik*.

And R' Chaim's troubles were not yet over. The strict justice meted out to him had not yet been satisfied. Measure for measure, twice over.

The *kollel* members expended superhuman efforts, a lot of persuasion, and an enormous amount of bribery, and finally the family's punishment was eased. They were allowed to leave Askashir and move to Vienna.

R' Chaim came to Austria a broken man, and died soon afterwards in poverty. When the *chevrah kaddisha* came to take care of him, the family did not even have the money for proper shrouds. R' Chaim was buried in Vienna in a temporary grave in a sackcloth, just as the Galicianer was buried in Jerusalem a year before.

A year later, the executive's body was brought to Israel, and he was finally put to eternal rest in Jerusalem by his family. For the British had conquered the land, and had annulled the decree of exile against the K. family. For after all, the trait of strict justice had nothing against them.

So What Do You Think of My Wolves?

FTER THE PASSING OF THE HOLY R' YISRAEL OF RUZHIN
on 3 Cheshvan 5611 (1851), his six sons took their places as
rebbes throughout Europe. The eldest, R' Shalom Yosef, lived
in Sadigur until his death that same year on 11 Elul. R' Shalom
Yosef's younger brother, R' Avraham Yaakov, then followed him to
Sadigur. In Chortkov R' Dovid Moshe ruled; in Hosiatin it was the
youngest of the sons, R' Mordechai Shraga; in Liova, R' Dov Ber. R'
Menachem Nachum went as far as Rumania, to the city of
Shtefenesht.

R' Menachem Nachum felt that it was providence that had sent
him to Rumania, a country very removed from the teachings of the
Baal Shem Tov. Through the years R' Menachem Nachum toiled,
trying to light a spark of belief in the hearts of his brethren, simple
farmers who, from the difficulties of exile and the travails of daily
life, had traveled far from their Father in Heaven. He tried everything, and when he realized that it was "miracles" that most interested these people, in their naiveté and innocence, he discarded his
cloak of secrecy to perform overt wonders. These marvels aroused
the Jews of Rumania and brought many of them closer to observance.

When R' Menachem Nachum reached Rumania, he was surrounded by a handful of *chassidim*; within a few years, thousands
followed him. For 18 years he served in Shtefenesht, and by the
end of his life he was known throughout the land.

One of R' Menachem Nachum's *chassidim*, a prosperous man
named R' Pinchas, was blessed with everything. G-d had granted
him wealth and honor and a wise and pious wife. Only one thing
was lacking, and because of this his riches were worth nothing to

him: The couple had no children. Many years had passed since their marriage and still their beautifully appointed house awaited the laughter and tears of a child.

At that time the miracles performed by R' Menachem Nachum began to create a stir among the Jews of Rumania, and were discussed all over the country.

R' Pinchas and his wife thought about R' Menachem Nachum's great miracles and came to the same conclusion: They immediately traveled to Shtefenesht.

The Rebbe gave them a half-hearted blessing: "May G-d help you." But because they did not realize that they should pay close attention to his wording, the pair returned to their home rejoicing.

After an entire year passed without a change, R' Pinchas realized that the time had not been propitious. He waited for Elul, the month of mercy, and before the High Holy Days he traveled once again to his Rebbe. There he asked for a blessing, "Please, a son, to learn Torah and serve G-d."

The Rebbe did not change his blessing. "May G-d help," he said, afterwards questioning him closely about his business affairs.

R' Pinchas returned home crestfallen. "We're not worthy," he cried to his spouse. "Obviously the Rebbe looked into my deeds and didn't find something which could receive a blessing."

His faithful wife heard his words and she, too, sobbed bitterly. That next year the pair tried mightily to improve their behavior. They were generous with charity, prayed fervently, and spent 12 months busily engaged in repentance and good deeds.

At the end of the year R' Pinchas and his wife again traveled to the holy court of Shtefenesht. R' Pinchas carried a letter of pleading to the Rebbe; his wife held onto a bag of money that was enough to sustain a large family for an entire year. They entered the *tzaddik's* room, put the request and the money before him, and cried, tears that could pierce the heavens themselves.

"Go back to your home," R' Menachem Nachum told them, his face alight with joy. "Today you have been helped. There was a decree against you, that you would not merit to have children, but repentance, prayer, and charity have annulled the evil decree!"

One year later, a son was born to them. Their happiness was

unbounded. R' Pinchas and his wife stood and thanked their Creator, Who had given them this enormous gift, and they spread largess to whoever was in need.

An icy, intense cold covered all of Rumania that winter. R' Pinchas, in preparation for a trip to his Rebbe for Chanukah, was packing his bags.

"One thing, my dear husband," R' Pinchas's wife said, pointing to the crib where their baby slept. "For several days I've been feeling terribly embarrassed. What haven't we done to thank G-d for this great gift? We've given meals to the poor, handed out charity. Everything is well and good. But one thing is missing, one vital thing that we've completely forgotten."

"And that is?" R' Pinchas asked.

"To thank the holy Rebbe, in whose merit we have a son!" the woman said quietly.

"And what do you think I was planning to do this trip?" R' Pinchas answered.

"No, that's not enough." The woman gave her opinion. "We all must travel to Shtefenesht, the baby as well, to show him to the Rebbe and get his blessing. Only in this way can we give him some small token of our thanks."

R' Pinchas jumped from his seat. "Can I believe what I'm hearing? You want to take a 3-month-old infant into this cold and snow for a journey of several days? The Rebbe does not have to see him to know how much we thank him. It's enough for me to tell him about the baby."

But his words fell on deaf ears. R' Pinchas's wife had already decided to join him on the trip. "We'll hire a closed carriage, protected against the cold. We'll wrap the baby in woolen blankets, and bring him to the Rebbe."

And when R' Pinchas saw that she was determined to do this, he surrendered.

The coach left in the early hours of the morning. The horses floundered in the deep snow, pulling the carriage heavily until they reached the main road. There their way grew easier, as the snow had been trampled down by the wheels of innumerable wagons.

The driver did not rest his horses until noontime. They then reached the edge of a large forest, and there the coach slowed down and eventually halted completely.

"Break time," the wagon driver announced. "The horses are tired and hungry."

They climbed out of the warm coach onto the frigid, snow-covered ground. They stretched their muscles, at the same time inwardly thanking the coachman for the much-needed respite: They were, indeed, famished.

When R' Pinchas's wife went to rummage for their foodstuffs, she felt the first stab of regret. The packages of food were all tied up together, and were located beneath the mountain of blankets that had been tucked around the infant to protect him from the cold. She had no choice but to take the bundled baby out into the cold in order to find the packages.

After they enjoyed a hearty repast, and the horses had been given their own feed, they once again climbed onto the carriage and continued their journey to Shtefenesht.

The rhythmic swaying of the coach from side to side, the heavy meal, the fatigue of the trip, all worked their magic: Eyes soon closed and R' Pinchas and his wife were both asleep.

The woman awoke first, confused. She glanced out the window and saw that night had already fallen; darkness was all around them. She reached immediately for the baby: The little one had not eaten for several hours! She fumbled with the blankets; searched one side, then the other, up and down.

The child was gone!

"Pinchas!" Her shrill cry pierced the interior of the coach. "The baby has disappeared!"

R' Pinchas, still heavy with sleep, awoke, his ears ringing. He rubbed his eyes and stared out at the blackness. "What do you mean, disappeared? You've buried him under a mountain of blankets. Keep looking."

"Pinchas, I've looked all over, in the entire carriage: The baby is gone!"

"Maybe he fell on the carriage floor?"

"I've looked there too," the mother cried in despair. "I'm afraid he's fallen out!"

"Oh, no!" R' Pinchas shuddered at her words. In an instant he stuck his head out of the coach's curtains and screamed to the wagon driver. "Our baby has fallen out of the carriage. Turn the horses around!"

At first the wagon driver thought R' Pinchas was joking, but when he saw the pair's deathlike pallor he hastily grabbed the reins, screamed out a few words towards the horses, and turned the carriage back in the direction from which they had come.

Their hearts were heavy with hopelessness; they could not think straight. They had no idea of what to do, had no clue as to when the baby had fallen out or where — on the right side of the road or the left, or perhaps in the center.

The wagon driver was the first to recover. He seated R' Pinchas on his right and the distraught mother on the left and said, "I will drive very slowly and look ahead of me. You keep a sharp eye out on each side of the road. Perhaps G-d will be merciful."

They did as they were bidden. The carriage moved slowly as they looked for a bundle on the snow.

They tried: one hour, two. They squinted in the deep darkness. But other than snow and trees they saw nothing.

"Who knows if the baby is still alive?" the woman cried bitterly. "It's been many hours that he is lying in the ice and cold, without a cover, only in his clothing. Who knows if he didn't freeze to death?"

"Hush!" R' Pinchas said angrily. "Don't even think such things."

They went on, their necks outstretched. Suddenly the wagon driver gave a shout. "I think I see something in the snow!"

The couple bent down and stared. Yes, the wagon driver was correct.

In the middle of the road, on the shiny snow, lay a small, well-wrapped bundle. But the bundle was not alone. Around it stood two black shadows: large wolves, their snouts looking up at them.

A shrill shriek came from the woman's mouth. "Oh, no! The wolves are eating our baby!"

R' Pinchas felt his heart come to a thudding stop. How much distress and trouble they had undergone until they had this child. Was all the pain nothing but preparation for this terrible moment, to see hungry wolves tearing up their beloved son? He gave a heartrending sob.

"Don't cry," the wagon driver lashed out at him.

"How can I not cry?" R' Pinchas's sobs grew louder. "Wolves are devouring my son! Wouldn't you cry if it were your son?"

The wagon driver brought the coach closer to the wolves and the bundle. The horses stopped short. The wagon driver's hand touched his passenger's shoulder. "R' Pinchas, look closely. You'll see there's no reason to cry."

And when R' Pinchas found the courage to look, he saw an unbelievable sight: The wolves had not only left the child unharmed, they were standing guard over him, licking him with their hot tongues to keep him from freezing.

"Two angels in the guise of wolves," the woman whispered, her voice trembling, staring at the sight.

When the wagon driver approached to pick up the "bundle," the two wolves silently disappeared into the forest.

"Thank you, L-rd. I must tell the Rebbe what happened," R' Pinchas cried emotionally, even while his sobbing wife was kissing her baby and holding him close to her. "A great miracle happened here! A Chanukah miracle! Who would believe it? Today, our child has been born once again."

They counted the hours remaining until their arrival in Shtefenesht. R' Pinchas planned over and over how he would tell the Rebbe of the incredible miracle. But he never expected to be greeted, even before he had a chance to say hello, by the Rebbe's joyful inquiry: "So, R' Pinchas, what do you think of my wolves?"

The Faith of a Gentile

THE WHOLE INCIDENT WOULD NEVER HAD HAPPENED IF Vladislav did not have the unpleasant habit of sticking his long nose into every conversation that took place around him. Whenever he saw a group of men chatting, whatever the subject, he felt a strong yearning to interrupt the talk and give his unasked-for opinion.

Vladislav Pudebenski, a farmer, son of farmers, a gentile, son of gentiles, was the epitome of hundreds of thousands of Polish peasants just like him. From daybreak he toiled in green fields, spending the hours until sunset among stalks of corn and piles of turnips. At night, he would drag his weary feet to the local tavern, to gladden his heart with a few shots of liquor. From here, from the other side of the shot glass, life looked completely different; much of the day's bitterness was erased with a few drinks.

After he had put away a few generous cupfuls (and, occasionally, whole bottles), he longed for a real conversation. After spending a full day with ignorant farmhands, whose only interest lay in blind obedience to their masters' orders, his soul desired a few words on topics a bit loftier than potatoes and cabbage heads.

A blast of cold air blowing in from the doorway announced the entrance of a new group of laborers into the tavern. Without conscious thought, Vladislav took one step, and another, until he found himself at the center of the loud group. The workers, it seemed, had just returned from the city of Alexander, where they had worked for an extended period building houses in the Jewish neighborhood. These Jews had paid well, and the workers, their hearts merry with drink, were reminiscing about their adventures in the nearby city.

Most of the conversation revolved around the mysterious figure of the *rabbiner* of Alexander: R' Yerachmiel Yisrael Yitzchak, author of the *Yismach Yisrael*. Most of the workers had heard of him through their Jewish employers; some had actually seen the secrecy-shrouded personality. The tales had whetted their fertile imaginations.

"I say he can't work miracles like our priest can," one tall man said ardently.

"Just the opposite: I saw the *rabbiner*. Listen to me, our priest doesn't reach the hem of his jacket!" a burly and muscular worker answered, no less hotly.

"Whaaaaat? To insult the priest?" several of his companions, devout Christians, shouted, their hands forming tight fists. A fracas erupted that could have ended in bloodshed, but Vladislav interrupted, yelling, "Friends, stop it, what's the use of this foolish quarreling? I'll prove that our priest is much greater than the Jewish rabbi!"

Silence descended. Everyone looked at Vladislav. One man broke the quiet.

"And how will you do that?"

"Nothing could be easier," Vladislav answered, totally excited by the brilliant scheme that had entered his mind that very minute. "I'll travel tonight to Alexander, dressed up as a Jew. Nobody will recognize me; not even this rabbi. And I'm sure I'll be able to get enough information to get some of those *Zhids* in trouble. We'll see if the rabbi can see through it!"

"Bravo!" Anti-Semitic sparks flew from the men's eyes. They congratulated the speaker and clapped him on the back. "We never thought you were so clever!"

"Wait here until I return," Vladislav answered, red faced from the generous compliments. "We'll sit here and share a drink and laugh at the *Zhids*."

When Vladislav left the village towards morning, he would not let anyone accompany him. He kept news of his departure, and the reason behind it, a deep secret from all but his new-found drinking cronies. The bundle that he held by his side contained some items of Jewish dress. These he had gathered together with great effort, effort made harder by the mantle of secrecy in which he cloaked his mission. "It's a good thing you have a Jewish-looking beard," one of the workers told him. "No artificial beard would look as realistic as yours does."

When Vladislav arrived at the forest near Alexander, it was impossible to identify him as a Polish farmer; even his mother would have been hard put to recognize him. The chassidic garb that he wore lent him a distinctly Jewish air. When he approached the city he joined in with a group of *chassidim*, walking with them to their holy Rebbe, R' Yerachmiel Yisrael Yitzchak of Alexander.

In his youth, Vladislav had lived near the Jewish ghetto in his town, and so he was able to stutter a few words in broken Yiddish. For one minute his heart almost stopped, as one of the *chassidim* began to question from where he had come. But help came from an unexpected source. "Don't you see that he stutters?" an elderly *chassid* flared out at the curious man. "You're embarrassing him in public!"

"I think this is the son of Chaikel, the baker from Shtefin," another mentioned. "He's Yankel from Setfin, whose tongue was burned with boiling water when he was a child, and who has stuttered ever since."

From that moment Vladislav — Yankel — became accepted as one of the crowd. Better not to embarrass him; best not to speak to him at all.

For a few days, Vladislav stayed in the city, his thoughts in turmoil. All the anti-Semitism that he had imbibed from childhood on was proved to be groundless. The Jews were revealed to him as completely opposite from the coal-black picture that had been painted in his mind, with the generous help of his parents and teachers. In all his days he had never seen hospitality such as that which he was enjoying now. The *chassidim* who felt such pity for stuttering Yankel never felt a moment's suspicion. In fact, the opposite was true: They took care that his every need should be met, lest he be forced to ask for something and thereby reveal his handicap.

He weathered some difficult hours when everyone gathered together for prayers. He had come equipped: He brought along a *tallis* and *tefillin* that he once found on the road, having seen them fall from a swift-moving carriage. He tried his best to copy his fellows' actions and movements, but all the same — It was no wonder that one turned to him and quipped, "What's the matter, Yankel, have you forgotten which arm you use for *tefillin*? Or have you switched to becoming left-handed?"

Vladislav required nerves of steel to achieve his goal. He waited the entire time for the chance to see the Rebbe, but it did not come. The Rebbe spent his day closeted in his room, and even when he joined them for prayers Vladislav did not succeed in getting near him. But the Polish farmer waited patiently for the right time, as a wild beast waits for the moment to pounce.

On Friday the bustle in the court grew more hectic than usual. Dozens of wagons loaded with *chassidim* pulled up, one after the other. Among the crowd, Vladislav could make out a stream of Polish-accented Yiddish, but to his consternation he could not understand a word.

When he saw groups of *chassidim* rushing towards the Rebbe's house, he was forced to stammer out a few words. "Why everyone run?" he managed.

"Don't you know?" a sweet-faced youngster with *peyos* dropping to his shoulders answered. "The Rebbe is 'giving *shalom*' to whoever comes!"

The blood pounded in Vladislav's temples. "This is what I've been waiting for five days already," he hissed between thin lips. An evil spark showed for one moment in his eyes.

He waited for a long time in the line that snaked through the entire length of the large court and reached the Rebbe's room. Contradictory feelings battled within him. He was happy that he finally had the opportunity to do that for which he had come; at the same time he was terrified of the Rebbe. During his five-day stay he had heard so much talk about the Rebbe's wisdom and insight, and though he did not understand all the words, he could clearly read the meanings from the speakers' tone of voice, their flashing eyes, the expressive gestures.

The line moved steadily; from hundreds standing before him now only a few dozen remained. Closer, closer, Vladislav-Yankel approached the Rebbe. He needed all his strength to keep his composure, but his tranquil face did not betray his churning emotions and pounding heart.

The *chassid* before him touched the Rebbe's fingers with trembling hands, mumbled "*Shalom aleichem*," in a whisper, and jumped away.

Now it was Vladislav's turn. He stood before the Rebbe. His knees buckled for a short moment, but he recovered and held out his hand.

The Rebbe's piercing glance stabbed right through him. "Eyes of fire," Vladislav thought, feeling weaker than ever.

The Rebbe's hand remained at his side. "Go to your death," he said in a sharp and final tone. Vladislav didn't wait to hear more of the "blessing"; he raced away on robotlike legs.

When he regained his composure, he thought, "Wow! Have I got stories to tell them back home!"

The *chassid* Elchanan stood a few paces away. He had stood behind "Yankel" in the line; now, he could not believe what he had heard. Had such a thing ever happened? Did the Rebbe actually curse one of his *chassidim*? And so crassly?

But clearly there must be some reason. And if the Rebbe said so, his words would be fulfilled, sooner or later.

Lightfooted as a cat, he followed "Yankel" to the home where he had been staying. He waited for him until he came out, his belongings tied into an unwieldy bundle with a heavy cord.

Yankel walked towards his village, never noticing the figure following him like a shadow. The two arrived — one a little behind the other — at a thick glade. Vladislav hung up his real clothing, the clothing of a Polish gentile, and began to cast off his chassidic garb. He removed the high boots, the black knickers, the white shirt, and high *yarmulke*.

A pair of unbelieving eyes watched his every move from between the thick leaves. Elchanan held his breath and stared, wide eyed, at what was happening. And now "Yankel" reached the last of his Jew-clothes: his arms tore off the *tzitzis* and flung them away.

At that same moment, "Yankel" crashed downwards like a tree felled by an ax. He lay motionless on the ground. His face, frozen in death, told its own story. Elchanan stood, paralyzed by the scene. Slowly he walked to the corpse and peered down at the glazed eyes and inert chest. Only then did he believe what he had seen.

He raced swiftly as a deer to the *beis midrash*, calling hundreds of *chassidim* to join him and see the miracle.

"The Rebbe told him, 'Go to your death,' and so he did!" the *chassidim* declared. The court was in a ferment; news of the Rebbe's "miracle" had taken wing, until it came to the ears of the Rebbe himself.

"You're wrong, it was no miracle of mine, and no wonder," the Rebbe explained ingenuously. "It was the power of faith alone, of that '*chassid*' who believed in my words. That was what brought down that gentile and killed him. A good deal of faith."

To Find an Honest Man

NO ONE COULD BLAME FELIX STRASSER FOR BEING distant from his Jewish heritage; he was a prime example of a *tinok shenishbah* (literally a "captured child," i.e. one who had no opportunity to learn of his Jewish tradition). His parents, simple, pious people, died in his infancy, and his uncle, his mother's brother, who was very far from observance, took him in and raised him as one of his own family. When Felix grew up, his uncle married him off to a woman from a partly assimilated Jewish family.

Felix spent his childhood years in the shadow of the Carpathian Mountains, in a typical village on the Marmush Plain. His memories revolved around endless days of work in the chicken coops and long hours milking cows in the barn. In that setting, no one noticed that Felix was blessed with an unusual flair for commerce. Only after his marriage, when he moved to a big city and broke away from his rural past, was Felix revealed as a gifted merchant who knew all there was to know about buying and selling. With the passing of time, Felix became an important businessman and his concerns flourished. When he felt sufficiently prosperous he opened a large textile and clothing store in the capital city of Bucharest.

His efforts met with great success and Felix could have lived in peace and tranquility, as his store became a nice source of steady and respectable income. But the rule that our Sages have told us — "If he has one hundred he wants two hundred" — was an apt description of this businessman. Felix would not be satisfied. He began to get involved in the manufacture of liquors, and he ultimately opened a factory.

The marvelous success of the Jew Felix was like a thorn in the side of his gentile competitors. They tried to impede his progress with all sorts of stratagems. More than one accused him of avoiding taxes, of selling stolen merchandise, of being in cahoots with smugglers.

In vain. Felix kept his hands clean. The police came to search his store several times, always leaving shamefaced. His businesses, it seemed, were above board and absolutely lawful.

"So we'll sit here, with our arms folded, and watch the Jew eat up all of our profits?" Steve shouted angrily. "Fritz, we've got to do something!"

Fritz Genishovski, the brains of the two partners in the firm Genishovski and Bolack Textiles, looked at his partner, Steve Bolack, in gloomy silence. It had been a long while since he had felt as terrible as he did right now. The Jew, Strasser, had managed to show them all up. His large textile store stood across from theirs on the city's main street, and in the short time since its opening, their profits had been cut in half!

"But you see, everything that we've tried hasn't succeeded. This Jew is as kosher as gefilte fish. Whichever way you check, he's pure olive oil," Fritz said in bitter scorn.

"It can't be! You're going to give in? You, Fritz, who created our business with your own two hands? Has your brain dried out?" Bolack returned angrily.

The two partners sat lost in thought. "I've got it!" Fritz finally shouted joyously. "Strasser's a spy!"

"Have you gone crazy, Genishovski? Strasser, a spy?"

"Absolutely," Fritz answered happily. "When the police find the incriminating documents that we'll hide deep in the drawers of his home there won't be a doubt about it. Felix Strasser will be imprisoned for the crime of spying for Russia!"

"And where are you getting those documents? And if you get them, how will you sneak them into Strasser's house? Good heavens, Fritz, you've gone mad!"

Genishovski chuckled and opened his briefcase. "With these," he said, waving a wad of bills in front of Bolack's astonished face. "These thousands can buy us the Mafia. And then they will do our work for us!"

The criminal organization did, indeed, do the work, with the care and efficiency for which the underworld is famous, leaving the partners open mouthed with admiration. Many incriminating documents were planted in Strasser's home. To complete the case, they set up a meeting with several so-called businessmen. Soon, all of Bucharest was agog! The merchant Strasser had been caught red handed, meeting with enemy agents!

Felix's case was set for trial. With the payment of a huge sum for bail, he was set free until the day of judgment.

How Felix had heard of the Rebbe, R' Yosef Meir of Spinka, author of the *Imrei Yosef*, was a puzzle. In any case, when a Jew is in trouble he somehow manages to find the right address.

When he arrived in the middle of the week and asked to be taken to the holy Rebbe, many wondered. What did this "goy" have to do with the Rebbe? Several people followed him to the door and listened to the conversation from outside.

"I'm facing a serious trial," Strasser poured out his heart. "They've framed me; there isn't a grain of truth to their accusations. But because the charge is spying, and there isn't a country in the world that isn't very sensitive about traitors, my clean past won't help me a bit. They've hired false witnesses, who will testify in court that I planned to sell state secrets to Russia. That is an absolute lie!"

There was silence in the room; the Rebbe, R' Yosef Meir, didn't say a word.

"They've told me that the Rebbe is a miracle worker. Please, make a miracle for me, that my innocence should be proved," Felix beseeched. He placed his hand into a bulging briefcase and brought out a large bill.

The Rebbe stopped him. "Do you keep Shabbos? In your house, your business?"

"How can I keep Shabbos?" Felix asked, surprised. His voice didn't hold a trace of either apology or confusion. "Most of my business is transacted on Shabbos. The Rumanian worker doesn't think about tomorrow; on Saturday he gets paid, on Saturday he goes to shop and spend his money. My stores and pubs are standing room only on Saturdays. To close on Shabbos would be the death knell for the business."

The door to the Rebbe's room burst open. Several of the *chassidim* who had been listening to the conversation in the hallway raced into the room ready to do battle with this insolent man. A Jew stands before the Rebbe telling of his Shabbos desecration without a pang of conscience, and actually has the temerity to ask for wonders and miracles! The *chassidim* waited for a sign from their Rebbe; one flick of the wrist and Felix would have been hurled out without another word. But the Rebbe sat quietly in his chair, looked at the man and asked, "And do you keep a kosher home?"

"Why should I lie to the Rebbe?" the man answered honestly. "My family is too busy to spend time looking for kosher meat. I buy what I need in the meat market and that's it."

"And *tefillin*? Do you put them on? Do you sometimes pray?" the Rebbe continued his interrogation.

"Who has the time and patience for that?" Felix answered, half innocently, half-defiantly.

The Rebbe sank into silence; everyone waited for him to speak.

"Let's do business," the *Imrei Yosef* finally said. "If you promise me that you will begin to pray, I promise you that you will be found innocent!"

"No, no, Rebbe," the merchant protested. "I can't promise that! How will I find the time to pray every day?"

A tense moment of expectant silence followed. The *chassidim* were certain that the Rebbe's patience would finally run out, and that he would order the burly businessman out of the room. Had such a thing ever been heard before? The Rebbe was offering him salvation on a silver platter; all he had to do was accept it — and yet he refused!

But the Rebbe didn't lose his composure. He gave the businessman a pitying look and in a tender voice said, "Do you know what? I will give you a pair of *tefillin*. Just put them on every day for a little while, for just a moment. If you promise me that, I promise that you will be found innocent."

Felix did the reckoning out loud, without a trace of embarrassment: "Just for a minute, once a day — *Nu*, it can be done! Rebbe! I promise!"

It was done. And the glowing face of the Rebbe, as he handed the bag with *tallis* and *tefillin* in it to the businessman, showed the boundless joy that only a mitzvah could bring.

Felix left for his home in Bucharest. And no one heard from him or knew of his fate.

A year passed.

Among those visiting the holy Rebbe's court was a Jew wearing a cap on his head, a pair of *tzitzis* over his shirt. He entered the Rebbe's room and left after a long while. Witnesses who stood nearby said that they had heard how the man had sobbed and begged the Rebbe for a means of repentance for his sins.

When the man left the room he sat down weakly on a bench and took a small volume out of his pocket. It was difficult, very difficult to recognize in the sensitive features of this Jew, who was reciting *Tehillim* so fervently, the visitor from the year before.

One of the *chassidim*, a particularly observant and curious one, gave him first one glance, then another, then stared at him again and again. Finally, he could not restrain himself.

"Tell me, aren't you the merchant from Bucharest?"

The man nodded his head in assent.

The *chassidim* gathered around, a flock of chirping birds, to give Felix Strasser their hands.

"But I'm not Felix Strasser," the man said.

"Who are you, then?"

"I'm not Felix," the Jew repeated. "I'm Fishel. That was my Jewish name. Now that I've returned to being a Jew, what do I need a gentile name for?"

"What happened at the trial?" the men asked impatiently.

"I was found not guilty. The defense managed to break through the wall of lies, and proved that the charges were groundless." And Felix told them of the entire affair, from beginning to its surprising conclusion, when, against all odds, he had been found not guilty.

"But how did you change so much?" one of the *chassidim*, more daring than the rest, asked.

"I owe it all to my uncle," Felix said. Everyone looked around in wonder; who was this uncle, and how did he fit into this remarkable story?

"My uncle who raised me did not learn Torah or observe the mitzvos. But he taught me something very important: Never lie! My uncle rarely hit me, but woe to me if I was caught in an untruth: What a whipping I would get! Because of this, I always kept my word.

"I had made a promise to the Rebbe, and so I began to put on *tefillin* every day. I would wear them for just a minute or two and then remove them. But after a while I began to think: It's one thing for a man who doesn't put on *tefillin*, but now that I put on *tefillin*, isn't it appropriate that I say a few words of gratitude and praise to my Creator, Who performed a miracle for me and saved me from the gallows?

"From that day on, I began to pray a little and speak with my Creator, a short but fervent prayer each day.

"But if I thought that was all, I was wrong. Again, my thoughts began to bother me: If I'm already *davening*, why shouldn't I do it as a proper Jew? And so I began to pray three times a day, with a *minyan*.

"Then I began to be filled with distress every Shabbos: Here I was, praying three times a day, but still desecrating the Shabbos? From that day on, my businesses were shut on Shabbos.

"But I still hadn't reached the end. Again, I did a reckoning: How strange, to keep Shabbos but eat nonkosher foods!

"And from the day I renounced *tereifah* foods, a new and purer spirit rested upon me, and I became, as you see, a new man."

The Prophecy of Yechezkel

THE TRAIN STATION IN GROSSWARDEIN WAS CROWDED with people. The platforms seethed with the hectic movements of baggage-carrying passengers, some racing to find a place on departing trains, others jumping from arriving trains and looking frantically around for a porter to take their heavy luggage off their hands.

Among the hundreds of people rushing back and forth was a woman who wandered hopelessly around, a piece of paper in her hand. Her eyes reflected a mixture of pain and hope; long years of suffering peered out of them, but a spark of faith also lit those tortured eyes.

"Perhaps you can tell me how to find this man?" She held out the paper to whoever was polite enough to stop for a moment and take a break from the frantic rush.

Several people looked but had no answer for her; finally, she stopped a Jew who looked observant.

"That's the new *dayan*, R' Pinchas," he said, surprised. "He lives in the Jewish Quarter of Grosswardein."

In a little while the woman had arrived at the home of the genius, the dayan R' Pinchas Halevi Tzimetboim, who was later to become head of the Grosswardein Beis Din.

R' Pinchas looked at the envelope that the woman pulled out of her bag and handed to him. His eyes immediately lit up.

"The holy Rebbe!" he murmured joyously. "The holy Rebbe."

This "holy Rebbe" was R' Pinchas's mentor, R' Yechezkel Shraga of Shiniva, son of the *Divrei Chaim* of Sanz.

To mark the occasion of the correspondence from his Rebbe, R' Pinchas donned his holiday finery, tied his *gartel*, and stood, in fear and reverence, ready to read the letter the woman had brought with her.

"The husband of the woman who brings you this letter left her 10 years ago. It is impossible to describe her sorrows. I ask of you, my dear student, to help her in any way you can to find her husband and have her set free."

The letter itself was crystal clear; the words spoke for themselves. And yet, the entire matter seemed mysterious and obscure.

"Where do you live?" R' Pinchas asked the woman.

"In the city of Brigal, in Poland."

"I don't understand," R' Pinchas muttered, rubbing his forehead in perplexity, "why should a woman who lives in Brigal, Poland, come to find her husband in Grosswardein, in Hungary?"

"I don't know either," the woman answered simply. "For 10 years I've been living in terrible solitude, and I don't know what to do," she burst out in tears. "My husband couldn't make a living in our town, in Brigal, so he decided to travel and try to find a means of sustenance far away."

The *dayan's* heart seemed to melt with pity. "And where did he go?"

"That's why I'm here, because I don't know where he went. He left and neglected to come back. A few weeks ago some friends suggested that I consult the holy Rebbe of Shiniva, and he commanded me to travel to Grosswardein and search for my lost husband."

R' Pinchas was relatively new to the city of Grosswardein. It was barely six months since he had arrived to sit on the *beis din*. He was like a stranger in a strange land, and knew only a few people there. But as a faithful *chassid*, he was filled with fervor: If his Rebbe had commanded this woman to travel to Grosswardein, there was undoubtedly a deep reason.

And nothing stops a faithful *chassid* in the fulfillment of his Rebbe's wishes!

R' Pinchas immediately left to arrange for the woman to stay in one of the city's inns. From there, he went to the home of the head of the *beis din*, the great R' Moshe Hersch Fuchs, author of the responsa *Yad Ramah* and one of the faithful students of the *Kesav Sofer*.

R' Moshe Hersch was not the leader of the city's *chassidim*, yet he was possessed of a firm belief in the greatness of the sages. Despite his wonder at the mysterious command contained in the letter, he, too, tried all he could to do the *tzaddik's* bidding.

The messenger of the *beis din* wore himself out that day. He galloped from the home of one innkeeper to the next, calling all the administrators of the local guest houses and owners of the inns for an urgent meeting at the home of the *av beis din*. When they arrived they were asked to immediately go to their inns and guest houses and find out if a certain Jew from the Polish town of Brigal was registered there as a guest.

After a few hours R' Moshe Hersch had his answer: The missing man was not to be found in any inn or guesthouse in Grosswardein.

Grosswardein was a large city, and R' Moshe Hersch and R' Pinchas knew that the wanted man could also be staying in a private house or unofficial guesthouse.

"It would be easier to find a needle in a haystack than to locate a Jew hiding in the city," R' Moshe Hersch sighed. "At least we should know for certain that the man is actually hiding in this town."

The next day the border guards were shocked at the appearance of their unexpected guests: two Jews whose countenances awoke in them a sense of awe and respect, not the usual sight in the offices of the border patrol.

The guards shuffled through the lists of those who had crossed the border; the man's name did not appear. He had not gone through their border, at least not recently.

R' Pinchas and the *av beis din* did not give up. When official sources proved unsuccessful they turned to the unofficial; from the open and legal they now checked the secret and illegal. In the next few days they carefully examined every inn in the city, including the most doubtful and dubious of houses. Then they checked the smugglers' routes, the paths that brought in tax-free goods. They generously bribed several men whose knowledge would have been greeted with joy by the local police commander, if only he had been able to get his hands on it.

But all leads proved fruitless; all hopes foundered on the hard rock of reality. The man was nowhere to be found; they knew for certain that he had never set foot in their city.

Up until now the two had worked feverishly, goaded by their belief in the sages. They were certain that if the Rebbe said to search in Grosswardein, the man undoubtedly was located there, and all they had to do was find him. But slowly their faith was dissipating.

And against that faith that was beginning to weaken stood the rocklike belief of the abandoned wife. Every morning after *Shacharis* she would come to the home of R' Pinchas to learn what had transpired the previous day. Every day, much to his sorrow, R' Pinchas had to report that no progress had been made. The *dayan's* already overcrowded daily schedule now included a few extra minutes, difficult minutes; a drop of bitterness was mixed in with his daily breakfast.

Twenty days of fruitless searches passed. R' Moshe Hersch felt that they had tried every possibility.

"Look," he turned to the *dayan*, when they were sitting alone together in the courtroom. "You must admit that we've done all we could, and there's just no sign of the man."

R' Pinchas nodded his head in agreement.

"If so, what is the point of keeping the woman in the city?" R' Moshe Hersch faced the harsh question squarely. "For three weeks we've been looking everywhere, and have come up with absolutely nothing. Why should we assume that the situation will change tomorrow or in two weeks? We have to tell the woman that we've checked everywhere possible, and it would be better for her to return to Brigal and stop wasting her time."

The words made sense; R' Pinchas, with his great desire to serve his Rebbe and fulfill his wishes, could not find any rebuttal to them.

The next day, when the woman paid her daily visit, R' Pinchas related the long account of every search that had been made. He ended with the words, "And so, it would be better for you to leave here and return to Brigal."

"No!" The bitter woman stood up before the *dayan*. "I will not leave this place until I am so commanded by the Rebbe of Shiniva. He sent me here, and only he can tell me to leave!"

With a heavy heart R' Pinchas sat down to pen a letter to his Rebbe. Yes, the *agunah* was right: The sage that sent her here was the sage that would send her away. He would tell the Rebbe that all their searches had led to nothing; the Rebbe would certainly tell the woman to return home.

R' Pinchas finished his letter and went to the post office to send it out express. He figured that it would take two days to receive a reply from Shiniva, and he would wait patiently for instructions on what to do for the woman.

The following morning the woman did not appear in R' Pinchas's home to find out her fate. The *dayan* wondered if she felt resentment towards him for having told her to return to Brigal. A dark cloud of melancholy shadowed his face.

Suddenly there was heavy knocking on the door. The *dayan* raced to the entrance.

"The *av beis din* has asked that you come to his home immediately," the messenger said, panting. "The matter can't be put off for even a minute."

R' Pinchas left his house and ran, his heart pounding, to the home of the *av beis din*. What could have happened?

When R' Pinchas entered R' Moshe Hersch's home, he shuddered. In the large room stood a burly policeman, forcibly holding a frightened Jew in his beefy arms. His eyes never wavered from his prisoner, ensuring that he made no attempt to flee. At his side, triumphant, stood the deserted woman.

"They say that belief in the sages is a great thing," the *av beis din* said in wonder, "and I say — indeed, a great thing! This is the woman — and this is her husband!" he announced, pointing in evident amazement at the panicky man standing in the policeman's grasp.

"How did he get here?" R' Pinchas hardly knew what to say.

The head of the *beis din* turned to the woman. "Tell us the story," he said.

The woman responded willingly.

That morning she had sat in the inn's dining room eating. Suddenly her renegade husband had entered, his clothing dusty and travel worn, his face weary. He approached a waiter and asked if he could get something to eat, not noticing the woman at all.

The woman waited for a moment to collect herself. Then quietly, ever so quietly, she had sneaked out through the back door. Once outside, she had raced directly to the local police station.

The *av beis din* took over the narrative. "The policeman arrested her husband and brought him to my house, at her request. The woman followed them silently. As soon as they entered, she began to shout, 'This is my husband, who left me 10 years ago!' " He turned to the man. "And now, you scoundrel, perhaps you want to explain where you've been?"

The man hung his head in shame and stayed silent. But the policeman succeeded in loosening his tongue.

The man had not been able to make a living, and had wandered here and there, trying to earn his piece of bread. That had been the situation in his hometown of Brigal. Finally, 10 years ago, he decided to seek his fortune far away. He traveled until he reached Bucharest, the Rumanian capital, and tried his luck there. But here, too, he was not successful. That was, after all, the lot of a lazy man.

The man, indolent by nature, did not bother to write to his wife and let her know that he was in Bucharest. For 10 years he wandered aimlessly around the city, living the life of a beggar.

Three weeks ago — on the day the woman had come to Grosswardein — a new thought came to him: How long should he wander around in this heartless city? He would travel to Hungary.

Who knew — perhaps riches were awaiting him in Budapest?

He did not have a penny saved. Over the next few days he begged coin after coin, and when he had enough for rail fare to the next stop he boarded the train. Thus he wandered from city to city, never traveling more than one stop at a time. He would get off, collect a bit more, and continue his journey. Until he reached Grosswardein.

On the train he heard that Grosswardein had a large Jewish community that was hospitable to strangers. There he would be able to fill his belly with a good meal.

The words fell on willing ears. He was hungry and thirsty, and he walked from the train station determined to get some food and continue his travels in a few hours or days. But his legs, and his destiny, had brought him to the inn where his wife was staying.

"It's what I said," the flabbergasted *av beis din* repeated, "They say faith in the sages is great — and it is, indeed, great.

"Think of it," R' Moshe Hersch continued. "The Rebbe of Shiniva knew, through *ruach hakodesh*, that on a certain day the husband would decide to leave Bucharest and travel to Budapest. The railway goes through Grosswardein, and it was there that he would stop and be directed to his wife!"

The amazing tale spread quickly through all of Poland and Galicia. On R' Pinchas's next trip to Shiniva he was besieged by *chassidim* who wanted to hear an eyewitness report.

They were still discussing it when the Rebbe of Shiniva himself passed by and asked what they were talking about with such fervor and interest.

"About the miracle of the *agunah* of Brigal," they answered.

R' Yechezkel waved a dismissive hand. "By *chassidim* everything is a miracle. I just figured that Grosswardein was a large city, and he would undoubtedly travel there."

So — was it a miracle or not?

The Thief of Tishrei

"A thief of Nisan and Tishrei
is not called a thief." (Sanhedrin 2b)

"ON ROSH HASHANAH IT IS WRITTEN, AND ON THE FAST of Yom Kippur it is sealed." The cantor's tenor, trilling upwards, could be heard a long distance away. The congregation in the Churvah Synagogue was deeply moved. Year after year the familiar words struck fear into the hearts of those praying. Sounds of weeping could be heard throughout the *shul*.

The man approached the house and stood near the door listening intently. Silence. He gave a furtive glance to the right and to the left: The courtyard was empty. Everyone was in *shul*!

Quietly he snuck in, walking on tiptoe, taking each step with infinite care lest he make any unnecessary noise.

"And repentance, prayer and charity annul the evil decree." The shout of the large congregation pierced the heavens.

He entered the room, quickly opened the bottom drawer of the dresser, and pushed all the clothing to one side. As he had guessed, the money and jewels had been hidden there. He grabbed all of it, not leaving a coin behind.

"A man, his foundation is earth and his end is earth; he wracks his soul for his bread," the leader of the prayers shouted hoarsely. All the congregants burst into tears.

As he was leaving the house, the "visitor" noticed some silver items. Gleefully he added the Chanukah menorah and the Shabbos candlesticks to the haul. He hoisted the heavy sack onto his shoulder and crept from the courtyard, not leaving even a footprint behind.

It was *Tzom Gedalyah* and the courtyard of the Churvah was all astir. Had such a thing ever been heard of before? A theft right in the middle of Rosh Hashanah, the Day of Judgment?

"Yesterday, after prayers, R' Shimon Levin went to his house and found the place emptied out. All of the money that he'd been saving for his old age, all his silver, was gone. Everything was taken," people told those few who had not already heard the news.

In his elder years R' Shimon Levin had traveled from Vilna, "the Jerusalem of Lithuania," to "the heavenly Jerusalem," the city within the ancient walls. The residents had accorded him much honor when he arrived in Jerusalem, as he was a respected and eminent personage, a scholar and a G-d-fearing man. He and his wife had come to spend their last days here. And now all their property had been stolen. What would become of them?

The city's important personalities, the rabbis and leaders of Jerusalem, gathered in the meeting hall of the Churvah courtyard to give the affair serious thought.

"First, we have to know if this is the work of a non-Jew, or if — " One of the city's philanthropists began, echoing the thoughts of many of those assembled.

"All the signs point to Jewish hands in this crime," a community leader answered grimly.

"Gentlemen, there is a terrible *chilul Hashem* in this shameful act!" the head of the *beis din* began to speak. "But if the thief was Jewish we shouldn't lose hope. We can use the power that Torah has on a Jew to compel him to return the stolen objects. We can threaten him with excommunication."

An official scribe who was present at the meeting was ultimately asked to fulfill his responsibility. He pulled out his inkwell and placed it on the table together with a sharpened goose quill. With a severe countenance that reflected the gravity of the situation, the scribe filled in line after line in thick black ink. When he was finished, all agreed that such a harsh decree had not been seen for many years.

"A Warning of the *Beis Din*!" the headline screamed. It was followed by verses of rebuke from *Parashas Bechukosai* and *Parashas Ki Savo*, and a list of dire curses that would befall the thief should he not return the stolen goods immediately. The warning was dotted with stern threats: "He will not live out this year," "He brings burning coals down upon his head," and the like.

All those assembled at the meeting had no doubt that once the announcement was printed and publicized throughout the city the thief would come, loot in hand, fall on his face, and beg for forgiveness.

But there was one among them who did not participate in the general feeling of satisfaction. He sat, a faint smile on his lips, his clever eyes clearly dismissing the awesome notice.

He was actually the youngest among the men, the genius R' Shmuel Salant, who had arrived in Jerusalem not long before and had immediately been accepted among the leaders of the city, not only because of his great knowledge and piety, but also because of his rare wisdom and acumen.

R' Shmuel's mocking smile did not go unnoticed, and those assembled demanded an explanation.

"In my opinion this notice is worthless," he said with a tranquil smile. "A thief who wasn't deterred from doing his vile deed during the Day of Judgment won't be afraid of the most frightful of declarations. He will continue to live happily in his home, undisturbed."

"And so what do you suggest?" the head of the beis din asked respectfully. He had already fathomed that it was worthwhile listening to the words of young R' Shmuel.

"I can suggest a solution, but only on one condition."

"And that is?"

"That you give me permission to do whatever I want, and whatever I ask you to do you'll do, without problems or questions — even if it seems very strange!"

The leaders of the community glanced at one another. A feeling of unvoiced approval settled upon the men gathered together. Permission was granted: R' Shmuel would have his chance.

R' Shmuel immediately commanded the two community caretakers to go to a certain man's home and bring him back, without giving him a word of explanation for the summons.

R' Mordechai the gravedigger was told to be there, his whip at hand.

And the rabbis and great men? R' Shmuel told them that when the man would be brought before them, they were to tell him that he must immediately return the stolen goods, or he would be put onto the table and whipped without mercy.

The rabbis demurred. "Do you have any proof that so-and-so is the thief?" one asked, voicing their unanimous sentiments.

"Didn't I instruct you from the beginning that you shouldn't ask questions or create problems?" R' Shmuel reminded them.

The caretakers returned, the man with them, pale and sweating. Nervously he scanned the assemblage.

The head of the *beis din* turned to him and emphatically demanded that he return the stolen items without delay.

"Gentlemen, I don't know what he's talking about," the accused said, his voice shaking with humiliation.

R' Shmuel gestured to the caretakers. They grabbed the suspect and placed him on the table, holding him down. R' Mordechai Shnitzer, the gravedigger, outdid himself with his blows. The man bellowed in pain and fear, but R' Mordechai, who had been previously instructed by R' Shmuel, paid no attention; the whipping continued.

"Leave me alone!" the man screamed. "I have something to say!"

R' Mordechai stopped and the man jumped down from the table and burst into tears.

"Gentlemen! What are you doing? You've brought an innocent man here, publicly shamed him, whipped him, and spilled his blood. Who gave you permission to do this? Do you want to kill an innocent man?"

A thick silence permeated the room. The rabbis looked at each other, perplexed. They had been prepared for a confession of guilt, not an attack. Some of them reacted by trying to appease the man. R' Shmuel was surrounded by unspoken looks of guilt and accusation.

But R' Shmuel was adamant, and did not allow the scene to last very long. The man's moving cries echoed through the room as R' Shmuel's voice commanded: "Start again." The caretakers dutifully lifted him onto the table and the whipping continued.

And again the man cried, "Stop! I have something to say."

He was taken down from the table. But the time for duplicity had passed. Gone was the man's truculence. Humbly, the man confessed. He was indeed the thief!

At R' Shmuel's behest, he revealed where the stolen goods had been concealed. The caretakers raced off and soon returned, bearing the loot.

"Was it *ruach hakodesh*?" the gathered men asked R' Shmuel in wonder. "To locate the man so unerringly and then to get him to confess?"

"Not *ruach hakodesh* and not a miracle," R' Shmuel waved his hand, as if to shoo away such nonsense.

Their astonishment grew. "If so, how did you do it?"

"With an observant eye," R' Shmuel smiled. "Yesterday, during *Mussaf*, I noticed that the man had disappeared for an extended period, that he was outside far too long. When he returned, almost at the end of the service, I looked at him carefully, and didn't like what I saw on his face. I didn't know at the time what it could mean, and so I kept quiet, but when I heard about the theft I immediately suspected him. I watched his reactions closely, and bit by bit pieced it together, until the entire picture was clear.

"And you see that I was right."

The Three-Stage War

THE SHUL WAS FULL; A LARGE CONGREGATION HAD gathered there for Shabbos morning prayers. The undiscerning eye would have thought it a normal Shabbos, no different from any other. But Asher'l Shechter, who knew everything that went on in the Tailors Shul in Zhvil, had hinted to friends, winking at them, as if to say, "There's news."

But when these men tried to obtain details he grew coy, and only after considerable pressure did he deign to say offhandedly, "Wait for the Torah reading."

Right after *Shacharis*, before the Torah was taken out, the *gabbai* climbed up the steps near the *aron kodesh* and announced, "In the name of the Rebbe, anyone who sends his son to school on Shabbos will, from this day forward, not receive an *aliyah*, even for a *yahrtzeit*. In addition, these people will not be allowed to lead the prayers until they have changed their evil ways."

The *gabbai* then descended. A storm immediately broke out, fiercer than any that had ever taken place there.

Baruch Segal was the city's most expert tailor. Leaders and noblemen took their place patiently in line until he deigned to sew their beautifully fitted clothing. His wealth was well known to all. Now he erupted at the *gabbai*, grabbing at his jacket lapel and shouting, "What a nerve! What is this? Next week is my father's *yahrtzeit*, and you won't give me *maftir*?"

The *gabbai*, a thin and frail Jew, paled beneath Segal's wrathful look. Yet a moment later, when he recovered his composure, he took a deep breath and returned the rich tailor's gaze with one of his own. "Absolutely not," he said firmly. "That's what the Rebbe, R' Shloimke, has decreed. As long as you persist in sending your children to school on Shabbos you will not get an *aliyah* nor will you lead the prayers."

Baruch the tailor seethed with fury. He needed every ounce of self-control he possessed not to raise his hand to the *gabbai*. But the mention of R' Shloimke had done its work.

R' Shlomo — R' Shloimke, as he was affectionately known — had only recently taken the place of his father. He was a man humble as Hillel, soft as a reed, one willing to defer to any Jew. Compliant and easygoing — except in matters of halachah and Jewish tradition. And particularly when the affair touched upon the soul of the Torah of Moshe — our holy Shabbos.

Recently the Russian rulers had passed a new law obligating students to go to school on Shabbos. No exceptions were allowed. The Jews of Zhvil planned to go to war against the awful decree. Studies on Shabbos entailed outright desecration of the day. Would they allow their children to desecrate Shabbos by writing and doing other forbidden tasks? Absolutely not.

But the men of means and influence, those on whom the simpler people had relied for support in having the decree annulled with negotiation and bribery, were the first to enthusiastically fulfill the czar's decree, thus weakening everyone's case.

R' Shloimke was still young, and had only recently ascended to his father's place, but when he saw the terrible breach about to take place in the wall that was Shabbos he prepared for battle like a fight-hardened warrior.

At first all of the city's rabbis gathered together to discuss what could be done and how to combat the wealthy men who had begun the breach. But news of the meeting leaked out, and the wealthy men sent their own delegation. In the course of the meeting it became clear that the wealthy men were standing firmly and unanimous in their position.

The rabbis stood still, as though their hands were tied. None dared risk an open confrontation with the city's wealthiest men. Those men had issued many threats, threats that held weight: They were, after all, the ones who held the coffers, and they intended to be the ones who made the decisions.

"The meeting can adjourn now," the young rebbe, R' Shlomo Goldman, announced. "I'll take care of the rest."

His colleagues, all of them older than he, were surprised at his words. But R' Shlomo continued to stand firm.

That day the Rebbe gave his aide a lot of extra chores to do, asking him to invite the *gabbaim* of every *shul* in Zhvil to his home. In those days every group of artisans had its own *shul* — tailors, blacksmiths, bakers, and leatherworkers. There was the *beis midrash* of the innkeepers, and one for the undertakers: more than 30 in Zhvil, and R' Shlomo made sure to include each one.

Strangely enough, no one refused the Rebbe's command, and that very night some 30 *gabbaim* sat ready to hear his words.

When he was finished speaking they stood shuddering before

him. "Does our rebbe want us to go to war with the city's most prominent citizens?" one of them demanded. "They are far more powerful than we are; if they want, they can report us to the government. This is a matter of life and death: If the government hears that the *gabbaim* of the *shuls* have come out against them, tomorrow we will be sentenced to hang!"

The young Rebbe gave the speaker a stern look, silencing him immediately.

"Don't be afraid," R' Shlomo told the group. "You're not fighting with my power; you are fighting with the power of Shabbos. I give you my faithful word: Whoever follows me, and is not afraid of those making the breach, will not be harmed by the government. And even if his brothers strike him, it is worth it for the sake of Shabbos."

The words were spoken with great determination. The *gabbaim* left the house absolutely convinced that what he said would be.

And the war began.

STAGE 1:

What the Rebbe expected came to pass. Not all of the wealthy men were cut from the same cloth. Baruch Segal, the tailor, gave in, partially because he was so unprepared for the announcement, partially because of the unswerving commitment of the *gabbai*. But there were many wealthy men whose anger was fired anew each Shabbos. Until now they had been favored with the most important *aliyahs* and had been given the honor of leading the prayers any time they so desired. Suddenly the way was barred before them: no *aliyahs*, no "amud." They had been thrown outside the pale, like something to be discarded because it was disgusting.

Malkiel the blacksmith, for one, was not too pleased. As usual on Shabbos, he waited for the *gabbai* to call him for his *aliyah*. And here it was, the end of the Torah reading and no *aliyah*, no *maftir*. Nothing.

His blood raced to his cheeks when the *gabbai* serenely told him that until his beloved son stopped going to school on Shabbos he would not receive any of these honors. Rabbi's orders. Malkiel was a hot-blooded man, and the path from his brains to his fists was a short one. Before the others had had time to blink, they saw the *gabbai* lying on the *beis midrash* floor, the blacksmith beating him in a murderous rage. If the congregants had not succeeded in separating the two, the rich man would have pounded the *gabbai* to death.

Similar scenes were repeated in several of Zhvil's *shuls* that Shabbos and the following ones. The town's tough men, accustomed to absolute obedience, could not swallow the revolutionary behavior among the *gabbaim*, who stood firm with remarkable unity and strength. The *gabbaim* relied completely on the Rebbe's strong words. "The Rebbe has decreed, and we will fulfill," one reassured the next during the difficult times.

The unwavering stance did its job. Several of the town's rich citizens could not bear the excommunication; they ceremoniously announced that their children would not attend school on Shabbos.

But the majority of the rebels would not surrender, continuing to send their children to school, despite the clear information that the students were being forced to desecrate Shabbos there: carrying, writing, erasing, tying, making crafts, and the like.

And what of the *aliyahs* and the leading of the prayers, so dear to them?

"Big deal," the rebels scoffed. "A person can live without 'shishi' (the sixth *aliyah*), and life is still good even without the cantor's lectern."

They were willing to accept anything, except to surrender before the Rebbe's determination.

And the Rebbe was, indeed, determined. After a few weeks the *gabbaim* were asked to give him the names of those who had not conceded. He quickly read through the list, and proceeded to stage two of the war.

STAGE 2:

Zhvil was a large city, and the *beis midrash* of the water carriers was its largest *shul*. The city boasted over 400 Jewish water carriers.

In those days water did not come from taps. Several sweet-water wells were located on the outskirts of the city, their source being the Slutz River. Here the water carriers would fill their jugs and bring the inhabitants their water supply.

Before *Maariv* that night, the *gabbai* made his announcement. "By order of the Rebbe, all water carriers in the city are invited to his home this evening. Everyone must be there."

Anyone who had ever seen R' Shloimke's shaky, tiny home in the Beis Yisrael neighborhood of Jerusalem would have found it hard to believe that before his move to *Eretz Yisrael* he had lived in a mansion in Zhvil. But even his gigantic residence could not hold all the city's water carriers. Therefore the carriers waited in his enormous courtyard to hear the Rebbe's words.

The Rebbe emerged from his residence and spoke. "I have the names of those who have refused to heed my command to take their children out of school on Shabbos. I will call out the names, and from this day forth I forbid any of you to bring them water. Whoever refuses," the Rebbe warned solemnly, "will not live out the year!"

The water carriers shuddered. The harsh words fell upon them like a heart-stopping roar of thunder. At first, in shock, they were silent, then a few of the more daring among them began to complain, in voices that grew louder and louder. Finally, two of the most brazen approached the Rebbe to voice their reservations.

"Our dear Rebbe, this command will have a serious impact on our livelihoods."

"How?" the Rebbe asked. "The list is in my hand; we're talking about 40 men. What are 40 men, no matter how wealthy, compared to the thousands in the city?"

The spokesman answered patiently: "Everyone knows that most of our income does not come from the simple folk, who pay a few meager coins for our hard work. Rather, we make our money from the rich, who order much larger amounts of water every day. These spoiled families are used to wearing beautifully laundered garments; every morning they have gentile maidservants come to their homes to wash the clothing. And for our service we are very generously paid."

The Rebbe accepted his words, but even so would not budge. "You've spoken properly, and I will compensate the water carriers for half their losses. You will have to take on the other half. If you rely on G-d for your sustenance, He will sustain you! But don't any of you dare to supply water to the rebels, or your end will be bitter!"

As soon as the word began to spread, pandemonium broke out in the city of Zhvil. The wealthy men carried on like lunatics. Bad enough the laundry — so their clothing would not be washed every day — but what about drinking water? Without water one cannot live!

They tried to persuade the water carriers with tempting offers, and even threatened them with government action. Nothing worked. The water carriers, like the *gabbaim* before them, were made out of good Jewish stuff — a stiff-necked nation.

The list of the rebels grew smaller. A fairly large group could not face the pressure and were removed from the roster of desecrators. But 20 still remained. R' Shloimke asked the water carriers for the updated list and headed to the third stage.

STAGE 3:

The dozens of members of Zhvil's *chevrah kaddisha* who had been invited to the Rebbe's home did not know the reason why. The more canny among them had guessed the background, but none of them could prophecy what the Rebbe would command. Perhaps he would tell them to bury the rebels outside the cemetery gates, or instruct them to demand a prohibitive price for a plot as a kind of rabbinic fine?

The men of the *chevrah kaddisha* did not wait in suspense for long. The Rebbe entered the room and characteristically went right to the heart of the matter, without hedging. After he read the list of Shabbos desecrators, he spoke. "From today on, if any of these men or their families are taken, you may not have anything to do with their burial. They will not be given a Jewish burial at all!"

The new command was publicized in the city overnight. People in the know added that the *chevrah kaddisha*, just like the *gabbaim* and water carriers before them, had been solemnly warned not to ignore the Rebbe's words.

The rebels laughed tauntingly and waved away the threat.

"We're all young and healthy; it will be years before any of us die. In the meantime the Rebbe's decree will be forgotten."

They and their friends laughed in public. In private, they carefully examined themselves to make certain they were absolutely healthy.

A few days passed. In the middle of Shabbos the son of the chief of the rebels was returning from school, his schoolbag on his back. He turned into a narrow street just at the moment that a speeding carriage, pulled by a mighty horse, was passing by. The frightened lad heard the sound of the horse's hooves; terrified, he tried to avoid the huge animal. But he was too late: The horse passed right over him, and the unfortunate young boy lay dead on the spot.

The father mourned his son bitterly, and when Shabbos ended he immediately called upon the *chevrah kaddisha*.

"With all of our sorrow, we cannot bury the boy," the head of the group explained clearly. "We must heed the Rebbe's words."

The bereaved father screamed and cried, begged for mercy, even threatened. The men of the *chevrah kaddisha* answered him briefly. "If you take your other children out of school on Shabbos, we will bury your dead son."

"Get out of my house!" the man yelled in fury. "I will bury my son with my own hands, and not give in to that barbaric Rebbe!"

It is one thing to talk and another to act. The boy's dead body lay in his father's home one day, then another. These were summer days, days of burning sun and soaring temperatures.

On the third day the father called the gravediggers and in a low voice announced his surrender, if only they would bury his son honorably without further delay.

And when the head of the rebels gave in, the entire movement fell apart. On that very day the rest of the men announced that they would no longer send their children to school on Shabbos.

The wall of Shabbos that had been breached had now been built and fortified anew. The Jews of Zhvil had seen that victory belongs to the most determined; and that their Rebbe, so humble and meek, was at the same time completely firm, when it came to the struggle for his beliefs.

A Spoonful of Cholent to Wake the Dead

THE WIND SHRIEKED, HEAVY CLOUDS COVERED A slate-gray sky, and a torrential rain poured down. The streets of Zhvil were deserted. No living being could be seen; everyone cowered in their homes, awaiting the storm's end. Everyone, that is, but the Jews, who at that moment were crowded into their *shuls*, immersed in the *Shacharis* prayers of Shabbos.

No living creature was on the street, until the ungainly figure of Stefan, one of the town drunks, emerged from within the fog. He walked heavily, sighed, and looked desperately around for some shelter from the raging storm. "If only I could find a cup or two to quench my thirst, everything would look better," the gentile murmured, trying fruitlessly to cover his head in the heavy downpour. From between the raindrops streaming down his face he occasionally stole a glance at the nearby homes. "Maybe I'll find an open door, a hospitable home," came the mutter from a throat that had gone without its beloved brew for several hours.

A pleasant fragrance suddenly wafted its way through his nostrils; the smell of the Jews' Shabbos food was drifting through the air and finding its way to the hungry drunk's nose. He stopped and sniffed, trying to find the source of the sweet smell. "I'm standing near the entrance to that warm home," he murmured beneath his mustache. "Let me go and see." With quiet footsteps — as quiet as a drunk could be — he approached the entrance, looking back and forth to make certain that no one saw him. The street was deserted. He pushed at the knob and, much to his astonishment, the door flew open.

"I'm lucky today," Stefan exulted, though his eyes searched to and fro as he was still fearful that the owners would appear from another room. But his luck held: The family was at *shul*, together with all of the city's Jews, and the house was totally empty. Dripping wet, he sat down at the set table and looked carefully at it. He saw a snow-white tablecloth and two covered challahs standing next to a simple glass cup. Most important of all, he spied a large jug filled with sweet red liquid. "Oh, lucky, lucky day," the gentile said to himself, not knowing where to begin. Perhaps with the fragrant challah? Maybe the sweet red wine? Or better yet, he could go to the oven that was giving off such incredible smells.

He was still mulling over the matter when he heard sounds on the street. A terrible dread gripped him. Perhaps the owners were coming. Without hesitating he tore off some large pieces of challah and stuffed them into his mouth. He grabbed the wine bottle with both hands and greedily downed half of its contents at once. The footsteps drew closer. In a panic Stefan retreated to the doorway, the challah in one hand and the bottle in the other. He tore off another hunk of challah and ate it. But in his haste the food went down his windpipe. The large piece was lodged in his throat like a rock. His face grew scarlet and then blue, a terrible groan escaped his lips, and he fell down, dead.

When R' Isaac and his wife approached their house, they knew immediately that something was wrong. The door was ajar, and they realized that they had neglected to lock it when they left for *shul*. "Oh, no, what a fool I am!" Isaac whispered in a panic. "Thieves must have gotten in." Carefully he stood by the door and listened. Absolute silence. "They must have finished the job and left. At least we won't be attacked when we enter."

Trembling, he tried to open the door, but it would not budge.

"Come here," he whispered to his wife. "I think somebody is holding it shut on the other side."

"Are you crazy, Isaac? Do you want to start with armed robbers, so that they will kill us?" his wife whispered back fearfully. But finally her husband persuaded her that thieves generally did not lock themselves in, and that they always run away with their loot.

Working together, Isaac and his wife pushed against the door until it opened. Apprehensively they entered and the woman immediately broke out into frightful screams. There on the floor lay a body, a man who had clearly choked to death.

"Who is it?" the woman asked in terror.

"I think it's Stefan, the drunk." He stared closely at the face of the corpse. "Yes, without a doubt, it's Stefan." A cold sweat beaded up on his brow. "He must have choked on the challah. Look how he tore it into pieces. Now I'm left without my *lechem mishneh*."

"That's what you're worried about, Isaac? We're in dire trouble: Soon all the gentiles will gather around and accuse us of killing him!" The woman wrung her hands and wailed. "If you don't do something, Isaac, our lives aren't worth a penny!"

"Should we throw him into the street?" Isaac asked, but he immediately had second thoughts. That was all they needed, that someone would see him dragging the dead body of a gentile from his house.

"Isaac, I have an idea," the woman said. "Run as fast as you can to the Rebbe and tell him about the trouble we're in, through no fault of our own. Maybe he'll have an idea of what we can do."

Like a hunted deer, Isaac raced to the home of the Rebbe, R' Shloimke of Zhvil. His house was the address for all those with problems; in such a time who wouldn't turn to him?

Breathing heavily, Isaac opened the Rebbe's door after knocking lightly upon it. Everyone knew that the Rebbe never locked his door; anyone who wanted could enter.

R' Shloimke was eating his Shabbos meal with his family, when suddenly Isaac burst in, screaming wildly. It took some time for the Rebbe to manage to make out what the man was saying. Then the Rebbe sank into deep thought. "It's a problem. The city is very tense, and not much time has passed since the last pogrom; if the matter comes to light they will kill Isaac and his wife, and other Jews, too, may pay with their lives."

Suddenly the Rebbe bent down and picked up a spoon from the table. He walked over to the tureen full of *cholent* that had just been removed from the fire. He filled the spoon with hot *cholent* and placed it in Isaac's hand.

"Return quickly to your house, and put the spoon in the gentile's mouth," he commanded.

Questions burst into Isaac's mind. He looked at the spoon; he looked at the Rebbe; he opened his mouth and shut it again. Finally he decided it was better to remain silent and do his Rebbe's bidding.

He swiftly walked through the streets, hoping that no one would notice him and ask embarrassing questions. Finally he reached his house. His wife was standing, trembling, in a corner of the room, a *Sefer Tehillim* in her hand and tears pouring down her cheeks. When she saw her husband her eyes lit up. "What did the Rebbe say?" she asked hopefully.

"The Rebbe gave me this," Isaac answered.

His wife stared at the spoonful of *cholent* in surprise. "The corpse can eat?"

"The Rebbe told me to do it and I will," Isaac said firmly. He approached the body lying on the floor and tried to open its mouth, but the man's lips were shut tight in the rigor mortis of death and Isaac could not get it to open. "Open your mouth," Isaac pleaded. "Look what I've brought you, Stefan, the Rebbe's delicious *cholent*. Rebbe Shloimke said you'd eat the *cholent* —"

Much to their shock, when the Rebbe's name was mentioned the corpse "obeyed" the request: The stiff lips opened wide. Isaac had been waiting for this, and he swiftly pushed the contents of the spoon deep into the open mouth and down into Stefan's throat.

The miracle took place right before the astonished eyes of Isaac and his wife: The dead Stefan opened his eyes, stood up quickly and without a look or a word left the house.

Their hearts beating wildly, the couple raced to the window to see what the resurrected gentile would do. To their unbounded wonder they watched the man walk down the street with swift steps, as if a moment before he had not lain before them, a dead man. He disappeared down the street.

Isaac ran in hot pursuit to see what would happen. When he approached Stefan he slowed down and with catlike tread followed him. The drunk walked like a robot, looking neither right nor left, taking even strides towards his home. After a short time he reached his house, opened the door with a strong shove, walked inside and immediately collapsed, dead.

Isaac strode back home to tell his wife of the miracle. She could not keep it to herself and ran to tell the story to her neighbors. Even before the city of Zhvil learned of the untimely death of Stefan the drunkard, the Jewish community knew of his resurrection. The reputation of the modest Rebbe, who normally concealed his powers but who used them openly when it came to saving a Jewish life, grew increasingly great. There were those who said that it was the publicity from this story that caused R' Shloimke to decide to go to *Eretz Yisrael*, where he settled in Jerusalem's Beis Yisrael neighborhood, living there from his arrival in 5685 (1925) until his death on the 26th of Iyar 5705 (1945).

A Mugful of Love

THE TWO DOORS OPENED SIMULTANEOUSLY. BOTH neighbors were early risers and were ready for *Shacharis* at the same time. The venerable R' Shachna and a guest walked out of one door. Across the hall stood R' Shmuel.

"Do you know who this Jew is?" R' Shachna turned to his guest. "The grandson of R' Moshe Kliers of Tiberias!"

"R' Moshe Kliers?" the other man said excitedly. "You must

hear a story about your grandfather, a story that has never before been published."

R' Shmuel had not even opened his mouth and he was immersed in the flow of talk from the voluble speaker:

"You're carrying your *tallis* and *tefillin* with you? *Nu*, obviously you're on your way to *daven Shacharis*. The tale I want to tell you also begins with a Jew hurrying to *Shacharis*.

"You're looking at me and wondering what a Jew from America has to do with R' Moshe Kliers? Well, today I am the rav of a large congregation in the United States, but in my youth I was a student in Jerusalem, sitting on the benches of the yeshivahs of Shaarei Chesed, learning all day and night. One morning I saw R' Avremel, one of the best students in the neighborhood, hurrying to sunrise prayers. Since he wasn't in the habit of *davening* at sunrise, I asked him, 'Why are you rushing?'

"'I don't want to miss the only bus to Tiberias,' he replied.

"'And what are you doing in Tiberias?' I asked as I ran after him.

"Between breaths he barked out short sentences, telling me that today was the *yahrtzeit* of R' Moshe Kliers and he had the custom of praying at the grave of the *tzaddik* every year.

"I lifted a curious eyebrow. 'What's a Yerushalmi Litvak doing at the grave of R' Moshe Kliers, the chassidic rabbi of Tiberias?'

"The young man halted his killing pace, pulled me into a corner, and whispered into my ear, 'R' Moshe Kliers saved my life, my future; he gave me a completely different perspective on life itself...' "

The noise could be heard in the distance. The squeaky bus rattled down the neglected roadway, clattering in a cloud of suffocating exhaust fumes. With a squeal that could set one's teeth on edge, it roared into the station. When it finally came to a stop, with a thunderous honk, one wondered if this bucket of bolts would ever manage to start up again.

"Get up quickly," the driver shouted in the direction of the passengers. "This old man still has to get to Tiberias today. *Nu*, there's no time to waste."

Near the bus stop a collection of passengers had gathered, the majority of them elderly, whose destination was clear: the city's famed hot baths. A small number of them were actually residents of Tiberias. And there was one more.

"Why is a Yerushalmi student traveling to Tiberias?" several of the passengers wondered. A few could not contain their curiosity and tried unsuccessfully to engage the young man with the melancholy eyes in conversation.

Avremel ignored the glances of his fellow travelers, determinedly staring at the words of the small Gemara open before him, trying valiantly to focus on the topic he was learning. No luck. Painful thoughts kept intruding, pulling his attention away. Against his will he found himself lost in a black reverie.

How many years had passed since his wedding, he asked himself in bitter scorn. How long had it been since the time that he had stood under the *chupah* and proclaimed, his heart thumping, "You are *mekudash* to me according to the law of Moshe and Israel." Years? No, only six months. Six months since that glorious day.

If one is successful, the years feel like days. But if not — A fire quickly began to rage, the fire of conflict and argument that was razing the foundation of his marital happiness down to nothingness. Yesterday, after yet another prolonged shouting match, one of an endless number, he had decided to flee to the farthest place possible.

"We'll separate for a while, try to find a way to heal the breach," he whispered to himself. And yet he had no idea how this visit to distant Tiberias would help repair his broken marriage.

Suddenly the epigram of the Sages appeared before his eyes: "Who is respected? He who respects others."

"Why are you looking for help in faraway places?" his conscience tormented him. "Help is right there in front of you, you just have to reach for it. If you give in a little bit, if you respect your young wife a little, you'll see how the situation will improve."

"No!" another inner voice argued stubbornly. "Let her appease me — she's the one who insulted me."

The trip took almost the entire day. Weary and aching after sitting for hours on the unyielding wooden benches, they finally arrived and descended from the bus. An orange sun lay low in the sky, coating the blue Kineret with blinding golden rays. The atmosphere was steamy.

With quick steps Avremel rushed towards a nearby *shul* for davening. After *Maariv*, he began to seek accommodations for the night. The other men in the *shul*, simple workers, suggested a moderately priced inn in the neighborhood.

The next morning he left the inn and found the *beis midrash* where the prominent men of the town *davened*. Sad eyed, he glanced at the other congregants. Among them he noticed an elderly *chassid* immersed in his prayers, his whole being clearly communing deeply with his Creator.

After *davening* the others came to him and warmly shook his hand. "Welcome, Reb Yid," they said.

A man with a radiant face walked over. It was the elderly *chassid* he had noticed earlier. The others had told Avremel that he was the city's *Rav*. "Where do you come from?"

"Jerusalem," he answered.

"Have you come to immerse yourself in the hot springs? Or do you have relatives here?" R' Moshe Kliers looked anxiously at this melancholy young man. Within minutes he had figured out what was troubling the lad, but he revealed no sign of it; but his perceptive, wise eyes radiated empathy.

Avremel mumbled something in reply.

"Come stay with me," the rabbi invited him with an expansive gesture. "You can stay as long as you like."

"Heavens no," Avremel blurted out. "I should bother the rav of Tiberias?"

But R' Moshe would not relent. "Why should a yeshivah student pay for a hotel when he can save the money he doesn't have?" Again and again he remonstrated with him; finally, Avremel acceded. He took his luggage from the inn, paid for one night's stay, and found his way to R' Moshe's home.

Avremel returned from the *beis midrash* late that night. He lay down on his comfortable bed in the rabbi's house and closed his eyes. The day's events raced before him. It had started with a wonderful *Shacharis davening* among those *chassidim*, who were com-

pletely disconnected from the world of the material. There was R'
Mendel Weg, whose intense concentration as he communed with
G–d caused the veins on his temples to bulge out like taut ropes; R'
Mottel Slonim, whose heart and very flesh seemed to sing to G–d,
a song of closeness and love; R' Aharon Yosef Luria, whose voice
when raised in prayer could melt even the stones around him.
Avremel had never witnessed such praying.

Avremel tried to sleep, after his exhausting day of prayer and
study, but slumber eluded him. From another room he could hear
a quiet hum: The rabbi was sitting and learning. Avremel felt
soothed by the sweetness of the tune. "How is it," he wondered,
"that the rabbi isn't too tired, after such a fatiguing day of learning
and teaching and all his other rabbinic duties?"

His thoughts wandered and flitted and, finally, he closed his
eyes and dozed.

A round ball of fire rose in the eastern sky, moved upward, and
finally bathed all of Tiberias in its golden rays. Avremel waited for
his host to accompany him to *Shacharis* . From the kitchen he
could hear the kettle bubbling; someone must be preparing breakfast. The fragrant smell of fresh hot coffee wafted through the
house. A moment later he heard the sound of the rabbi's leather
shoes. The rabbi walked into his bedroom, a cup of steaming hot
coffee in his hand. "Good morning," he greeted the rebbetzin.

A look of wonder passed momentarily over Avremel's face.
Then he dismissed the incident from his mind.

That night he did not hear the rabbi's humming.

"Oh, even the rabbi is still only human, and sometimes gets
tired —" he thought to himself.

A sudden slight noise sent Avremel out of bed to investigate.
He tiptoed to the door of the rabbi's study. A small kerosene lamp
cast its dim, reddish hue upon the rabbi's face. He was sitting and
writing diligently; the fountain pen's metal tip raced swiftly over
the pages. Occasionally he would dip it into an inkwell that
stood nearby.

Suddenly the rabbi halted, his high domed forehead wrinkled

in concentration. He stood up and took out an old *sefer* from the bookshelf, scanned through it briefly, and then returned to his writing.

"The rabbi is responding to halachic questions, and here I thought he was asleep!" Avremel chuckled in amazement.

The next morning saw yesterday's scene repeated: the hot cup of coffee being served to the rebbetzin, the heartfelt and pleasant "good morning."

"How awful," Avremel's conscience smote him, "the rebbetzin is ill, and here I am taking advantage of the rabbi, so that he has to serve two of us!"

After *davening* he rushed back to the rabbi's home, packed his luggage, and went to say goodbye.

"Why are you rushing away?" R' Moshe asked. "Haven't you enjoyed your stay in my home?"

"It's better for me to go back to the inn, and not bother the rabbi," Avremel justified himself.

The rabbi was puzzled. What was the problem?

"I happened to notice that the rebbetzin is ill," Avremel explained, blushing.

"What are you talking about?" the rabbi looked at him questioningly. "Thank G-d, the rebbetzin is perfectly healthy."

"But I saw myself how the rabbi has been serving the rebbetzin, bringing her coffee to her room each day!"

The rabbi chuckled mildly. "I do that every day."

Avremel fell into a bewildered silence.

"It is said in the name of the Arizal," the rabbi said, a small smile lighting up his face, "that every Jew must take upon himself, every morning before prayers, the mitzvah of loving one's fellow as he would himself. How can one fulfill this mitzvah? Just by feeling in the heart? No, you have to do something practical. And why should I search far away when I can fulfill the mitzvah here in my house? Do you understand? I'm not 'serving' the rebbetzin, I am simply honoring her. That's the difference!"

The innocence and simplicity of the words pierced deeply into Avremel's soul.

The great rabbi of Tiberias carefully bringing the cup of hot coffee to his wife each morning? Did he lose his self-respect by the gesture? A lightning bolt of comprehension struck the Yerushalmi yeshivah student. "What am I doing here? Why should I be looking to go far away? I can fulfill the mitzvah of loving my fellow right at home!"

The packed luggage stayed packed. Avremel decided to return to Jerusalem immediately, to rebuild his home from the foundation up. Tears ran down his cheeks as he bid farewell to his gracious host, the man who had opened his eyes and taught him a lesson greater than he had ever learned in all his life.

The Meat Grinder

THE CITY OF ORSHIVA IN RUMANIA WAS A SMALL ONE; its Jewish community, too, was small, consisting mostly of plain, simple folk. There were a few respected families, among them the Schwartz family. The dynasty began in the days of the grandfather, R' Yitzchak Isaac Schwartz, who came to the Rumanian city straight from the benches of the Pressburg Yeshivah, where as a young man he learned from the *Kesav Sofer*.

While R' Yitzchak Isaac was a great Torah scholar, he did not want to use his learning as his means of livelihood. The verse, "If you eat the fruits of your labor, you are fortunate and it is good for you," was his credo. With his arrival in Orshiva he began to get involved in its world of commerce. In those days the sausage industry was just beginning to flourish, and several sausage factories had opened throughout the world.

R' Yitzchak's business talents soon became apparent. He quickly learned the secrets of the trade. In order to delve further into the business, he traveled to America to explore the rapidly developing factories there. Heaven smiled upon his endeavors: He charmed the owners of the large sausage plants and these tight-lipped men, who guarded their manufacturing secrets so zealously, opened their factory gates to the young European with the Jewish garb.

R' Yitzchak learned quickly; things that someone else needed a month to study he would master in a day. He swiftly absorbed the industrial secrets revealed to him and understood them clearly. Those plant owners who had taught him their most confidential processes did not lose on the deal; conversely, R' Yitzchak, in his brilliance, suggested some serious improvements in the process which cost them almost nothing. Things came to such a pass that in many far-flung cities throughout the continent factory owners waited for the Jewish guest from Europe who, it was said, was nothing short of a miracle worker.

When R' Yitzchak returned to Orshiva after a sojourn of two and a half years, he was equipped with considerable knowledge and confidential information. He did not wait long; he immediately took huge loans from several banks in the large cities, using as collateral the dowry that his wealthy father-in-law had given him, his large home, and other valuables that he had inherited. When he had the money in hand he bought a large plot of land at the edge of the city, hired several dozen diligent workers, and soon the city of Orshiva could proudly boast of its "Schwartz Sausage Factory."

Success smiled down upon him from the first day. Almost from its inception the business showed a healthy profit. R' Yitzchak put all of his many talents and boundless energy into the factory, all the knowledge and tricks of the trade that he learned in America, and almost all of his strength. An abundance of siyata *dishemaya* seemed to pour down upon the factory; there was a blessing in all its wares. Schwartz's Sausages became a universal favorite throughout the land, thanks to its unusual, spicy taste and trademark, mouth-watering aroma. In a short time, R' Yitzchak became a wealthy man.

R' Yitzchak put almost all his strength into the business; almost, but not quite all. The teachings of his youth were not lost to him. He faithfully found time for daily Torah study, and when the factory expanded and he added more men to the work force he hired a foreman who spent the entire day in the business. R' Yitzchak was then able to find more free time, and ultimately he spent most of the day in learning.

With the passing of years R' Yitzchak gained a name as a G-d-fearing businessman, one whose hand was always open for a mitz-vah, one of the area's most generous philanthropists.

R' Yitzchak could have sat back in serenity and enjoyed two bounteous tables, that of wealth and that of Torah study, if not for the aggravation of his only son, Reuven. The youth was well known for his exploits, and not for the good. He daydreamed away his years in elementary school, thinking only of his father's factory, spending long hours fantasizing on what he would do when he inherited it from his father. This apple has obviously fallen very far from its tree!

"I won't be lazy like Father," he would think to himself. "I won't stay in the *beis midrash*, letting some stranger take care of my business!"

As he grew older Reuven continually embittered his father's life. He refused to go to yeshivah, hated the study of Torah, and it was only with great reluctance that he agreed to put on *tefillin*. He would spend his day at the factory chatting with the non-Jewish workers, and would often go with them to swim in a nearby river. When he told his father that he wanted to marry the daughter of one of those non-Jews, his father threatened to disinherit him, to cut him off without a cent. Against his will Reuven finally married a Jewish girl.

Not long after his marriage Reuven completely gave up all signs of Torah observance. He even discarded his Jewish name: Now he was Isidore, and woe to anyone who accidentally called him Reuven.

For some years R' Yitzchak saw his life in ruins around him. To outsiders, he attempted to keep up the facade of tranquility, but within the depths of his heart he sobbed over the terrible humiliation inflicted upon him by his only child. When people came to tell him that Isidore had spent Yom Kippur in a *tereifah* restaurant his heart gave out; he died on the spot. That day he was buried in the old cemetery of Orshiva.

After the *shivah*, which Isidore, gritting his teeth, was forced to observe, he immediately fired the plant foreman. "From now on I'm the only boss here," he announced to the bewildered workers. He then proceeded to fire all those workers who observed Shabbos.

A new era began. Schwartz Sausages, once the symbol of unswerving *kashrus*, now turned out *tereifah* products made from *tereifah* animals. Jews who kept kosher tried not to pass by the factory, and stayed away from the neighborhood altogether.

Years passed.

In the year 5671 (1911) a new, young rabbi came to the city. This was R' Yoelish Teitelbaum, son of the holy rebbe R' Chananiah Yom Tov Lipa of Siget, author of the *Kedushas Yom Tov*. Orshiva was the first city in which R' Yoelish served as rav, before he traveled to Kroli and Satmar. Immediately upon his arrival the 24-year-old rabbi began to concentrate on raising the consciousness of Torah within the city. First he opened a yeshivah and began to teach. Slowly he brought the authority of Torah to a higher level. There were many such as Isidore, eager to leave the teachings of their fathers, and the rabbi was forced to fight many battles. It seemed to be a lost cause: The majority of the city's citizens still identified with Reform and only a handful of G-d-fearing Jews remained.

At that time Isidore was on the verge of marrying off his eldest son. Rumor had it that there would be mixed dancing at the wedding. The rabbi, hearing the tales, announced: It will never happen. Everyone looked forward anxiously to the wedding; most had no doubt that the rabbi would be defeated in the coming debate. What was a young, fanatical rabbi against the successful entrepreneur whom all feared and obeyed?

As dusk fell a messenger, out of breath, arrived at the rabbi's home and interrupted his *shiur*. "It's begun: There is mixed dancing at the wedding."

Rabbi Yoelish closed his Gemara with a sigh. He donned his coat and, accompanied by two students, headed for the wedding.

When the rabbi and his students entered the giant, elegant hall, silence fell upon the crowd. The glowing countenance of R' Yoelish did not mix well with the boisterous throng. The sounds of singing and dancing ebbed away.

R' Yoelish stood upon a table. "The Torah strictly forbids men and women to dance together," he announced in a firm, loud voice that could be heard in every corner of the hall. His eyes glowed like hot coals. "Whoever dances like this will pay dearly for it."

A frozen silence lay heavily on the room. The circles of dancers immediately broke apart.

The father of the groom raced, scarlet faced, towards the rabbi. "You've come to destroy my affair? We'll continue to dance as we please, men and women together!"

"There will be no mixed dancing here," the rabbi thundered. "I will not allow it."

Isidore seethed with fury. "There shall be!" he planted his feet firmly on the ground. "No fanatic rabbi will tell us what to do. Let the dancing continue," he growled to the guests.

"If you listen to me, all will be well," the rabbi answered calmly. "If not, you will pay a high price."

Isidore was beside himself. He longed only to show his guests how unimpressed this fanatic left him. "And what's the high price I shall pay?" he asked mockingly.

The rabbi favored him with a frigid glance. "You will be ground up."

"Did you hear?" Isidore burst out into raucous laughter. "You've all heard what the rabbi has said. I'll be ground up. Ha, ha, ha."

Wild laughter broke out throughout the room, following the rabbi as he walked out of the hall. The father of the groom and his guests could hardly contain their mirth over the strange rabbi and his stranger words.

The merry wedding ended near daybreak. Hundreds of revelers finally made their way home. Isidore and his wife, too, went home to rest up. But Isidore was a hard worker, and a few hours of sleep sufficed for him. Early in the morning he ran to his factory to keep an eye on the manufacturing process. His slogan had always been, "The business comes before all." In his haste he put on his elegant clothing, the suit he had worn the night before at his son's wedding.

When he walked into the plant he was dumbfounded: The workers, not expecting the boss to show up on the morning after his son's wedding, were standing around chatting; the machines were silent.

"All workers to their places!" Isidore shouted angrily. With a fearsome visage he approached the giant meat grinder and pressed the button. The huge blades began to turn with breathtaking swiftness. Isidore found the worker whose job it was to handle the grinder and pushed him towards the machine in order to get him to do his job. The startled employee, frightened by the sight of the giant whirring blades, grabbed his employer by the edge of his elegant suit jacket.

Isidore furiously watched his wedding suit grow stained. In disgust, he gave the worker still another shove. The panicky man pushed back.

Suddenly a horrifying scream echoed through all the walls of the factory. No one could tell just how, but the boss's suit had somehow gotten tangled up in the swiftly turning blades. In unbelievable suffering and pain, Isidore died under the machine's relentless blades.

"The rabbi warned him yesterday that he would be ground up if he wouldn't stop the mixed dancing, and so it came to be," everyone whispered during the melancholy funeral. "The rabbi is indeed a holy man!"

The astonishing story made its way swiftly through the region, and from then on the people trembled before the words of the rabbi, whose name became celebrated throughout the land. The face of the city, too, was changed beyond recognition, and when R' Yoelish left Orshiva after about 14 years, he left behind him a thriving Jewish community.

From Istanbul to Nuremberg

TWO FIGURES WALKED THE CITY STREETS. ONE WAS A young man of about 30, with long, golden *peyos* reaching down almost to his shoulders. His blue eyes seemed to emit sparks of holiness though he preferred to keep those holy eyes lowered, so that they saw nothing more than the four cubits surrounding him. The sharp-sighted could have made out the golden stripes of his Yerushalmi kaftan that showed out just a little from beneath his long black coat.

Escorting the young man was an olive-skinned youth, his face clearly showing his complete subjugation to the man striding beside him. His manner of walking, his entire countenance, exhibited his readiness to do whatever the golden-haired man asked of him.

Figures such as these were unusual in the human scenery of the city of Nuremberg even when times were good — and now times were not good. For in the year 1933, the Nazi Party had captured power in Germany and had placed the evil demon, Hitler, may his name be blotted out, at its head.

Immediately upon his ascension to power the cursed being began to put into effect the ideas he had written about in his book. The government quickly began to tighten their grip on the Jews and, as a first step, to persecute every Jew for being a Jew.

The two men were newly arrived visitors staying at the home of R' Aharon Marcus. They were unfamiliar with the city and did not know their way around.

"Excuse me," the escort, R' Moshe Yaakov Frankel, asked a passerby. "Can you show us the way to the rabbi of the city?"

"*Ja*," the man replied, pointing the way with characteristic German politeness. "There, around the corner, is the home of *Herr Rabbiner*."

The men made their way to the home of the rav of Nuremberg, the *gaon* R' Avraham Yitzchak Klein, who welcomed his exalted guest happily.

"*Shalom aleichem* to the Lelover Rebbe," he burst out in joyous tones. "I've been waiting for you a long time."

"I am no rebbe," the other objected. "I am the son of the rebbe of Lelov, R' Shimon Nosson Nata, may the *tzaddik's* memory be blessed, who was called to the Heavenly Yeshivah three years ago."

The rabbi was not overly impressed with the objection. The reputation of the young man, who served his Creator with unparalleled devotion, had reached his ears. The Jews of Nuremberg had followed the young man's behavior closely, seen his holy ways. This young rebbe of Lelov, they said to each other, was a man who promised to reach new heights. But those really in the know understood that R' Moshe Mordechai did not have to reach new heights. He had already scaled the highest mountains of spiritual accomplishment: As a very young man he had already experienced the revelations of *ruach hakodesh*. The world would indeed have marveled had they but known his abilities. But, like his grandfather, R' Dovid of Lelov, before him, he had prayed that such powers remain hidden from others, and so it was.

After the visit to R' Klein's home, the rebbe and his escort walked back towards their host's house. The street was quiet, but suddenly a rowdy gang of youths burst out of a tavern, singing drinking songs and yelling Nazi slogans.

"Hitler Youth," the frightened whispers went from one to another, and suddenly the street was deserted. Such youths, pressed into service by the accursed leader when he first came to power, were notorious, and more than one person had felt the blows of their fists. And if their victim was Jewish, as almost all were, it was almost inevitable that he would lose an eye or a tooth — if he was lucky. If he was not, whole limbs might be left mangled.

The thugs looked up and down the deserted street with satisfaction; the sight of the people fleeing from before them was like a refreshing breeze.

Suddenly the bullies stopped, thunderstruck.

Two men wearing long coats, their *peyos* and beards clearly identifying them as Jews, were walking tranquilly down the street, as if panic and fear were concepts unknown to them!

The gang members immediately fell into a murderous rage, like bulls reacting to the red cape waving before them. They gave off satanic yells and lunged towards the two.

R' Moshe Yaakov Frankel was, in stature, the exact opposite of the rebbe. The rebbe was slight and frail, while he was broad shouldered and strong. In a fleeting thought he made the reckoning: "At least I can manage to take some beating without being harmed. But the rebbe? His body is weakened from his frequent fasts; he'll surely fall beneath the very first blow!"

With his broad body R' Moshe Yaakov tried to shelter the thin frame of the rebbe, while at the same time returning blow for blow and then some, fending them off with his fists. The bullies were stricken with panic: They were not used to Jews hitting back. The tables were turned: In another minute several large bodies fell, bloodied, beneath the steely fist.

The wail of a Gestapo car put an end to the battle. Several uniformed men jumped out of the automobile.

"Holy rebbe, run away quickly!" R' Moshe Yaakov whispered. Before the brave young man could move he was handcuffed. He tried to tell the "forces of the law" what had happened, but the outcome was a foregone conclusion. The Gestapo was not interested in the truth. It was Jewish blood they wanted, not the broken, bloody bodies of a few German thugs. R' Moshe Yaakov had not finished his first sentence before he was roughly thrown into the car.

If the incident had taken place a few years later, most likely he would have been shot on the spot, but at the time these events took place, the Nazi monster did not yet dare to bare its claws so clearly. Thus, R' Moshe Yaakov was only taken under heavy guard to prison. Three charges were made against him: attacking innocent German citizens, attempted murder, and disorderly conduct.

He spent an entire week in a dark and musty jail cell. All his attempts to contact the outside world were fruitless. He was promised that an attorney would come to him — but the promise, naturally, was never kept.

Heartbroken, the rebbe left R' Moshe Yaakov, his protector and shield, behind. He immediately turned to the community leaders, its rabbis and wealthy men, and they did all they could to free the young man imprisoned for the sin of having protected himself from two-legged beasts. But nothing worked: R' Moshe Yaakov had disappeared into one of the city's prisons and no one could say where. Thus a week went by.

With the approach of Shabbos the Jews of the city begged the rebbe to hold a chassidic *tisch*. Though he had not yet taken on the customs of a rebbe, seeing their sincerity, he gave in to the pleas.

Friday evening. The *shul* was crowded with hundreds of congregants, their eyes raised to the exalted form of the rebbe. A chassidic *tisch* was an unusual sight for them, and the masses, thirsty for spirituality, eagerly drank up the revitalizing waters of Torah and *Chassidus*.

First the rebbe sang, in a voice both sweet and uplifting, the words of "*Shalom Aleichem*" and "*Eishes Chayil.*" Then he poured wine into a goblet, as if preparing for *Kiddush*.

The rebbe took the goblet in his hand, closed his eyes in devotion, then returned the goblet to its place. Complete silence fell upon the *beis midrash*; everyone held their breath as the rebbe began to tell the tale:

"Thousands of *chassidim* bid farewell to their teacher and rebbe, the holy R' Moshe of Lelov, who had decided in the twilight of his days to leave his birthplace of Poland and go to *Eretz Yisrael*. 'I will go to the Western Wall and scream, until all the Jews in the world wake up and come, together with *Mashiach*,' he told his family and his *chassidim* again and again.

"The ship spent a few days in Galtz, a Rumanian seaport. The captain explained to his passengers that in the absence of a proper wind they would be unable to sail. On *Motzaei Shabbos*, R' Mendel,

R' Moshe of Lelov's aide, left the boat and went to the city to buy food for the journey.

"A pleasant wind began to blow stronger and stronger. The great sails that had until now drooped weakly from the masts suddenly took form; the boat began to shift in the water.

"'We sail now!' the captain announced. 'With the help of the wind we'll be able to leave port on our way to Kushta.'

"R' Moshe of Lelov and his sons, R' Elazar Mendel and R' Yitzchak Dovid, pleaded with the captain to wait for R' Mendel, the faithful servant of the family. But the captain refused to heed them, answering angrily, 'Everyone knows that when we await a wind it's prohibited to leave the ship. Whoever does so, does it at his own risk, knowing the ship may leave without him. I can't hold back an entire ship, with its hundreds of passengers, for one lone person. Your friend,' he added, 'can take the next ship out and join you later.'

"None of their arguments did any good: The ship sailed without R' Mendel. It took six days to reach Istanbul, the Turkish capital. R' Moshe was melancholy. He knew that R' Mendel had not disappeared by coincidence; there was something behind it. He walled himself up behind a barrier of silence, occasionally giving out a deep and bitter sigh.

"On Friday night the rebbe finished his prayers and stood to make *Kiddush* on the wine. He filled his goblet and stood — for three solid hours. His face grew alternately red and pale. It was clear that he was undergoing some terrible spiritual battle, fighting a vicious war against the forces of evil. Finally he put the goblet down on the table.

" 'By my faith, I shall not make *Kiddush* until R' Mendel is here!' he said with conviction.

"At that minute a terrible wind broke out, a turbulent wind that tossed the ship back and forth like a tiny speck on the sea. The waves seemed ready to draw the ship into the blackness. Suddenly, with a terrific bang, the door flew open. The unconscious figure of R' Mendel fell into the room before them.

"At the end of his days R' Mendel revealed that his disappearance had not been a coincidence. All the six days he was gone he had been imprisoned by some demonic powers, and had wandered like a madman through the streets of Galtz, walking wherever his feet happened to take him. 'On Shabbos eve my strength gave out,' R' Mendel said. 'In my weakness I leaned on one of the houses, and then I heard "them" speaking. "What can we do; the old one is destroying worlds, we must return him —" At that moment a wind began to blow. I felt as if I were flying in the air; suddenly, I landed on the deck of the boat. The rebbe had saved me from their hands!'"

In the *shul* in Nuremberg the crowd stood still, completely engrossed in the story told by the young rebbe of Lelov. If a fly had dared enter the room, one could have heard the buzz, so thick was the silence.

The rebbe stopped speaking and waited silently for a moment or two. His face shone as he began to speak again.

"And I too, like my grandfather before me, tell you: I shall not make *Kiddush* until R' Moshe Yaakov Frankel is here with us again!"

A terrible fear fell upon the assembled; everyone held their collective breaths in tense expectation. Suddenly the people realized that this young man wearing a *shtreimel* and standing at the head of the table was being revealed to them as one of the great men, like those of previous generations, a worker of miracles whose holy powers could change the course of nature.

The *tzaddik* stood and waited, but not for long.

The door of the *beis midrash* suddenly flew open; in the doorway stood the figure of R' Moshe Yaakov Frankel. His face was white and he was trembling. He approached the rebbe, whose face glowed with joy.

"Holy rebbe," R' Moshe Frankel burst into tears, *"a gutten Shabbos*. Hashem has performed a miracle for me. All week I've been in prison. I said '*Vidui*' and I have died a hundred deaths in my heart. I awaited the hangman with every passing hour. A little while ago a top Gestapo officer came to my room and told me I was free to go. I didn't believe it: I thought he was playing with me and would certainly shoot me in the back as I left the cell. I walked out, my face to him, but no, his words were honest, and here you see me, standing before you!"

A miracle!

My Hands Will Find Him

THE DOORBELL RANG. A YOUNG BOY WENT TO SEE WHO was at the door, and a postman immediately asked him to call his father or mother.

"Registered mail," the postman explained. "I need a signature."

Her heart thumping, the woman of the house scribbled her name and immediately closeted herself in her room.

"What we have been fearing has come," she murmured heavily. "We've always been afraid of this letter."

The letter was curt; its words cold and cruel:

"Mr. Yehoshua ben Moshe, you are hereby requested to repay your debt of… Failure to repay this amount within the stated time shall result in legal action."

She cast a worried gaze over the room, at the peeling walls that had been in need of a new coat of paint for years, at the rickety furniture with its shabby fabric. The entire house screamed of poverty.

"*Nu*, when Yehoshua comes home tonight, I'll have something to cheer him up with," she laughed bitterly. She sat for a long while, her head hanging, lost in melancholy thought.

It had been some years since they had found themselves awash in mounting debt. They were blessed with eight children, wonderful children, but to support such a household was no simple affair. The father worked from morning to night. Maybe it was bad luck, maybe G-d had another reason; in any case, none of his businesses flourished. It seemed that the more he worked the less he made; his salary hardly paid for one quarter of the mammoth expense of supporting 10 mouths.

Finding no choice he had tried a new "business": borrowing. He borrowed from this one to repay that one. But as is the way of borrowing, before you know it you find the rope tightening around your neck. One day he opened his eyes and there he was, submerged beneath a stormy sea of debt. There was no way out.

In his anguish he sprang to reckless action. His reasoning was swift, and stupid: So-and-So, a wealthy Tel Aviv black marketeer, lent out money at exorbitant interest rates. He would borrow a large sum, and use it to pay off all the smaller amounts due.

"And what happens after that?" a small voice in his heart asked firmly.

"*Mashiach* will come," he returned, "or I'll get a better job, I'll work night and day, I'll win the lottery…"

For a short time he breathed a sigh of relief: The humiliating requests, the endless sneaking about, the avoiding of shops and men in the *shul* had come to an end. After an extended period of walking with shoulders bowed, he could finally hold his head up proudly again, he could meet the gazes of his fellow men.

But his happiness was short lived. He learned, too late, how wise were the words of the Sages: "Interest is like a snakebite: It makes a tiny puncture in the foot, and one doesn't even feel it; suddenly everything is swollen and hurting. So too, one does not feel the interest, and suddenly he has lost a great deal of money" (Rashi on *Parashas Mishpatim* 22:24).

The loan shark, a hard and impatient man, began to embitter his life. When the time came to repay the debt he began to receive threatening letters from attorneys; finally, the document threatening legal action came.

"How will you leave me alone with eight children?" his wife argued in the course of a heated debate with her husband.

The thought of fleeing abroad had occasionally flitted through Yehoshua's mind; now that the shadow of the courts hung over him, and the fear of prison tore through his heart, he had decided to immediately travel far away until the affair had been forgotten. His wife's pleas were fruitless, as were her protests that she would be the one to wind up in jail instead of him.

The next day Yehoshua fled the country. No one came to say goodbye; with a bitter heart he boarded the plane to Brazil.

Upon his arrival Yehoshua had his name changed; not, as was customary, because of serious illness, but rather to take on a new identity in a large Brazilian city. He became a part of the Jewish community there, finding a job as a *shochet*, the trade he had had in Israel as well. The letters that he would send from time to time to his family informed them that he was doing well. At the beginning he sent large sums of money home with his letters.

And then his letters stopped arriving. At first his wife thought it was some temporary problem, but when his silence became prolonged she tried to discover what had happened to him. No one in the community could help find him. No one knew if he was alive or if he had, heaven forbid, been murdered by the bloodthirsty gangs who used to hang around in the nearby gentile neighborhoods. A heavy curtain fell on Yehoshua; he was as one lost in the void.

Days too heavy to bear fell upon the *agunah*. A thin thread had connected her to her husband, and now that thread had been severed. She was ready to forgive him for all he had put her through, just let her see him alive once again, she prayed.

But there was no response. No word.

Two and a half years passed. Michoel, the eldest child, was soon to be bar mitzvah. His uncle, his father's brother, took him under his wing and prepared him for the occasion, and even bought him a fine pair of *tefillin*. But it was not enough: Three days before the celebration, his sister-in-law turned to him and burst out in tears: "Bad enough that I'm an *agunah*, but my son will be known as an orphan. Everyone will point their fingers at him and say, 'Look, there's the son of the one who ran away, the one who didn't even bother coming to his own son's bar mitzvah.' "

Her words pierced the heart of her brother-in-law, R' Menachem, like a sharp, flinty arrow. That very day he went to seek counsel of the great rebbe of Lelov. His legs took him to a humble apartment in the large building on Rechov Rabbi Akiva in Bnei Brak.

"Only he," he thought hopefully, "only the rebbe of Lelov can do something."

What that "something" would be he did not know. But he was possessed of a strong faith in the Sages, and he was certain that he could rely on the rebbe, whose powers were awesome.

"Holy rebbe," R' Menachem wept, "the trouble is great and the humiliation even greater."

And the rebbe, his heart always at one with the grieving hearts of his fellow Jews, stood up and began to pace the room in agitation. Menachem's heart pounded wildly. Finally, the rebbe turned to Menachem and said, "He will surely come to the bar mitzvah. Don't be afraid of the moneylender; when he comes, bring him to me immediately."

That night the rebbe did not go to bed; he remained shut up in his study until the late hours of the night. No man knew, no man saw what he was doing. Just the sound of his shoes tapping on the floor back and forth, back and forth, hinted at a lion pacing his den. From time to time his pleasant voice could be heard, mixed with tears and pleas.

On that night Yehoshua, too, in a far-off land, could not sleep. He tossed and turned in his bed for hours, but sleep eluded him. His thoughts suddenly flew thousands of miles away, to his small, simple home in Bnei Brak.

"What's come over me?" he wondered. "Have I forgotten my family completely?"

As the hours passed, his uneasiness intensified. With dawn's first light he jumped frantically out of bed and hastily packed his bags.

Two days later, on the day of the bar mitzvah, the startled family members were awakened at dawn by a loud banging on the door. When they opened it they could not believe their eyes: The missing father, the husband who had disappeared, stood before them. When Yehoshua entered, pulling his valises after him, it seemed to them that he had stepped out of a dream.

"What are you staring at?" Yehoshua asked with an embarrassed smile. "I'm back."

"Abba! Right, you came home because tonight is Michoel's bar mitzvah?" the youngest chirped out in her reedy voice.

Yehoshua almost fell down in a faint; he was too ashamed to admit that he had actually forgotten.

A few hours later Yehoshua and his brother, Menachem, stood trembling in the rebbe's home. Yehoshua went in to speak to the rebbe for a short time. At the end of the conversation he left the room, his eyes reddened and swollen from prolonged crying. Menachem then entered.

"Did the rebbe grab him by the *tzitzis* to bring him back for the bar mitzvah?" Menachem asked hesitantly.

The rebbe's blue eyes rested upon him, his glance a mixture of sternness and pity.

"This I can say: I spent an entire night searching for him throughout the world, from one end to the other, until I found him. And from now on he will take the high road, both in the physical as well as the spiritual realms."

The Erev Pesach Prayers

R' TZVI ZELDOWITZ AND HIS WIFE, MUSHKEH, WERE AMONG the most respected people in Minsk. G-d blessed them with wealth and honor; He didn't stint on anything. He even gave them an only son who proved to be an unusually gifted lad. R' Tzvi would constantly pray that he would merit the traditional blessing of raising his son to Torah, to the *chupah*, and to good deeds.

He prayed, but he did not merit it.

R' Tzvi was still in his prime when he was stricken with a serious illness. After only a few days he passed away, a relatively young man.

His only son, Eli Baruch, was still a youngster. At his father's funeral he tore his shirt and made two blessings: *Baruch dayan ha'emes* and *Baruch ha'tov v'hameitiv*: The one on his father's demise; the other on the wealth he had inherited, for he was now a very rich young man.

"What will a young man like this do with such wealth?" the Jews of Minsk wondered, hoping that the merit of his father and his respected family would stand him in good stead and help him walk a path of reason and not one of hasty, reckless deeds.

The week of *shivah* ended; the 30 days of mourning passed. Eli Baruch returned to school. But his face seemed to change; one could see that something unhealthy was going on inside.

His mother, the widow Mushkeh Zeldowitz, felt some kind of change in her son's behavior, though she could not quite articulate what it was. Mushkeh's mother, who came to live with her bereaved daughter after the tragedy, also noticed something, but the two women assumed it was a result of the terrible trauma that Eli Baruch had suffered due to his father's death.

They had no idea that even during the days of the *shivah* a group of tough youths had held a stormy meeting to discuss Eli, the wealthy heir. This was an outsider fringe group among Minsk's fine

Jewish youth. The leader of the gang, Yisrael Temkin, known as Srul, had decided, with the majority backing him, that when such a treasure fell into the innocent hands of an inexperienced youngster, it would be a crime not to take advantage of him. It was the time for action.

With the end of the week of mourning, Srul Temkin and his gang waited for Eli Baruch as he passed them on the way to yeshivah.

"Hey, gang, look who's there."

"It's Eli Zeldowitz himself!"

"Did you know that Eli has just gone through a tragedy?"

"What are you saying? Let's go cheer him up."

Eli heard the exchange, realized that they wanted him to hear it, and ignored them completely.

He bypassed the raucous boys playing among the trees, hitting each other with thin branches and exchanging insults. What did he have to do with them: He was a yeshivah student, sitting and learning Torah, and they were idlers wasting their hours on nothingness and frivolity.

Srul raced after him. "Hey, Eli, why are you running away from us?"

Eli looked behind him. He shot a suspicious glance at Srul's sweaty face, at the modern hairstyle that reached almost to his eyes.

"What do you want?"

"Why are you angry with me? I haven't done anything bad to you," Srul said, laying a friendly arm on Eli's shoulder. "Let's sit and talk a little; the day has just begun."

Eli followed him listlessly. The gang members received him with warmth and joy, sat him down in their midst, flattered him with soft words and oily phrases.

That day Eli was half an hour late for his class.

The next day Srul and his gang once again accosted him. This time Eli was more forthcoming, and actually sat and talked for an hour.

Without his knowing, Eli fell deeper into the trap. The young men, who were his own age, hypnotized him with false words that inflamed his youthful imagination.

"Why should you stay in yeshivah, within its ancient walls and old books?" they challenged. "Tomorrow, and every day after that, all the charity collectors will be at you, sucking your blood, forcing you to help every sick person, every widow and orphan and poor bride, and you'll find yourself a pauper. With us, no one will ask for charity; you can use your money for your own pleasure, for trips, for parties, whatever you want!"

Day after day they sought to persuade him. And their words had an impact on his naive and inexperienced heart. The poison flowed; suddenly he felt himself full of a deep hatred for the yeshivah and all that was in it. In particular, he despised all the charity collectors that came to him.

His loved ones were still trying to decide what to do with the top student who was falling more and more behind, when suddenly the terrible news hit Minsk: Eli Baruch Zeldowitz had strayed onto an evil path, had left observance completely, had joined the good-for-nothing group of youths who hung around the outskirts of the city.

Each day Eli distanced himself more and more from his family. He loathed everyone who kept Shabbos and mitzvos, and since the Zeldowitz family were all firmly counted among the G-d fearing, the young boy stayed away from all of them without exception. He was estranged even from his mother and grandmother, barely concerned with their welfare. It looked as if in a short time the youth would leave his mother's house and make his home among the gang members.

These were the days of Nisan. Pesach was approaching; in the home of the widow Mushkeh mourning prevailed. "Not enough that I have lost my husband, shall my only child be taken as well?" she cried, brokenhearted.

All the family members got together to discuss what could be done about Eli. They decided to approach him pleasantly, rather than using a stern manner.

One evening Eli returned from the streets, tired and surly. A guest was awaiting him: his uncle, R' Dov Zeldowitz. He greeted the sulky boy with love.

"Eli, my dear, are we going to have the pleasure of your company at the *Seder*, as we do every year?"

Eli's face darkened. "I know what you all want from me!" he shouted angrily. "You just want my money!"

R' Dov was sorely tempted to slap his nephew hard on each cheek. Instead, he steeled himself, reined in his anger, and laughed out loud. "Eli, you're talking foolishness. I need your money? Me?"

R' Dov Zeldowitz, indeed, had no need for his nephew's wealth. He had merited both great Torah scholarship and vast holdings, and every year he hosted his entire family in his spacious and luxurious home.

Eli realized the silliness of his words. Still, his bitterness overcame him. "I'm not coming to the *Seder*," he told his uncle brutally.

"And where will you be?" His uncle, frightened, asked him.

"In a place where I won't be forced to eat dry matzahs and drink diluted wine for seven days," the youth taunted him.

"Where will you be?" his uncle grabbed his hands.

"In the Swan Hotel."

"Oh, no!" his uncle cried. "That gentile hotel? The one that serves only *tereifah* food?"

"That's right," the young man chortled. "I want to eat everything, drink whatever I like. No one will force me to drink four cups of vinegary wine and eat rock-hard matzah balls floating in lukewarm chicken soup. I want to eat everything, whatever I want, without any limits!"

R' Dov backed away like someone standing before a snake. His shouts of horror could be heard throughout the house. "Woe to us, our Eli has become a complete gentile. Help our Eli!"

At the sound of the shouting, Mushkeh Zeldowitz and her mother appeared. They burst into tears at the sight of Eli, their beloved Eli, gathering all of his belongings into a fine leather knapsack. "Good luck, my family," he mocked. "Eat matzahs and *kneidlach* until they're coming out of your nose. I'm spending the holiday in a hotel, together with Srul Temkin, my good friend, and the rest of the gang. We'll party, we'll dance, we'll enjoy ourselves. We're young and all of life is ahead of us."

Mushkeh grabbed her only child's hand. "Eli, my dear, have pity on your mother. I bore you beneath my heart for nine months. Come to your uncle for the *Seder*. You won't regret it."

The youth gave his mother a distant glance. "Recite the Haggadah for me too," he said. He left the house with large strides, ignoring the pleas of his mother and grandmother.

R' Dov stared after the disappearing boy with a stern face. The widow's sobs pierced his soft heart. "We'd better do something before it's too late," he murmured to himself.

The leaders of Minsk were called together that night for an urgent meeting. The members of the Zeldowitz family at that time held some of Minsk's most prestigious positions. The scholar of the clan, R' Baruch Zeldowitz, was the head of the Minsk Kollel which collected money to maintain the men of Minsk who were now learning in *Eretz Yisrael*. At the end of the discussion it was unanimously decided to send off a telegram to the holy city of Jerusalem.

It was the night before *bedikas chametz*, the twelfth of Nisan 5657 (1897).

R' Naftali Tzvi Porush, the secretary of the Minsk Kollel, came home early that evening. Preparations for the holiday were in full swing. His wife and daughters were busy polishing the doors and windows, cleaning the closets, scouring the tables, scrubbing the chairs.

While she worked feverishly to finish up, R' Naftali Tzvi's wife told him that one of the Kollel executives, R' Leib Cohen, had come looking for him several times, and it seemed from the tenor of his words that it concerned something urgent.

When R' Naftali Tzvi heard that, he immediately went out. He walked quickly to R' Leib's home.

The executive showed him a telegram that had been received at noontime in his house, signed by the head of the Minsk Kollel, R' Baruch Zeldowitz.

The telegram was only two lines: "Eli Baruch ben Mushkeh has gone on an evil path. Please pray for him urgently."

The standing of the head of the Kollel in those days has no parallel in contemporary times. The Jerusalemites lived from the philanthropic donations of their Kollel counterparts abroad. They shared a strong mutual bond. The head of the Kollel was almost like a ruler of a miniature state. And R' Baruch Zeldowitz came from a family which had always generously supported the Jerusalem community.

R' Naftali realized that if an urgent telegram arrived asking for prayers, the situation must be a grave one. Though few details were given about Eli Baruch ben Mushkeh, he realized what he had to do.

Immediately after *bedikas chametz* 10 members of the Minsk Kollel went to the Western Wall.

R' Naftali Tzvi, R' Leib Cohen and his two sons, and six other scholars from the Minsk Kollel left the Mishkenos Yisrael neighborhood where R' Naftali lived. They stopped at Yemin Moshe to pick up R' Shlomo Zalman Porush, R' Naftali's father, who also served as an executive of the Minsk Kollel.

They were all deeply moved; they felt the importance of the hour and the heavy responsibility that had fallen upon them. They walked down the dirt path that wound through Mt. Zion at the edge of walled Jerusalem. The path was dark; a black canopy hung over their heads, with thousands of flickering lights dancing above them, bringing mysterious greetings from the cosmos. A light spring breeze patted their cheeks, carrying in its wake the enchanting fragrance of the budding fruit trees that mingled with the smell of baking matzah.

"I wonder who this Eli Baruch ben Mushkeh can be," one of the young men said curiously. "And what story lies behind the urgent telegram."

"That's not our job," R' Shlomo Zalman told him sternly. "We have only to do that which is requested of us: to pray that the Creator send down upon this man a holy spirit, and make his path a proper one."

His words fell upon receptive ears. The group reached the small, unlit plaza in front of the Wall. They lit a candle and prayed fervently for the salvation of a Jewish soul.

Their hearts held a pure motive. "Master of the Universe, receive the prayers of the sons of Jerusalem, and sanctify G-d's Name through His ruined city. Let our brothers in the Diaspora know that the prayers of Jerusalemites are not returned unanswered."

And their prayers flew higher and higher, towards the Heavenly Throne.

At that very hour, after a day spent indulging himself with the others, Eli lay down on the hotel's comfortable bed.

He tossed and turned for some time. And suddenly his terrified figure could be seen racing out of the hotel like a man fleeing a blaze.

Mushkeh and her mother awakened in a fright to the sound of banging on the door. "Mother, open up, it's me, Eli!" the boy called.

But after his behavior the other night, the women were not enthusiastic about the homecoming. "Go away, you insolent boy," they called, convinced that his gang of toughs was waiting with him on the other side of the door, planning on stealing their possessions and harming the two unprotected women.

The boy continued to bang on the door, begging his mother and grandmother to open it, but they stopped answering him.

Despairing, he circled round the house, waited a few moments, and then quietly tapped on the window of his grandmother's room.

The elderly woman felt her pity stir. She carefully walked to the window and spoke to the boy from behind the closed shutters. She understood from his words that he had undergone a real transformation, and that he hoped that the gates of repentance would be opened before him, along with the gates of his own home.

Still suspicious, she hesitantly opened the shutter a crack to see if the boy was backed up by the thugs. No, he was alone! When the grandmother saw her grandson's tormented face, she realized that he had undergone a radical metamorphosis. She let him in and explained to her daughter what had happened.

Eli fell into his mother's opened arms with choking sobs. "Mother, forgive me for having pained you," he said brokenly.

When he calmed down somewhat he revealed what had happened. "I went to bed in the hotel's suite. I was tired from all the frolicking, but I couldn't fall asleep. Suddenly I saw the figure of Father, may he be blessed. It was as if he was alive, and speaking to me, with a stern face. 'Eli, my son, go home now, repent, change your ways.'

"Time and again the frightening image returned, until I realized that this was no dream. Suddenly I felt a terrible wave of regret. I felt like a drunk waking up from his stupor. 'Oh, Master of the Universe, how low have I sunk?' I looked with disgust at the horrible room, got dressed, left everything behind, not wanting to spend an extra minute in that terrible place."

On the first day of *Yom Tov* the town leaders used to visit the home of R' Eliezer, the "*gadol*" of Minsk; on the second day they would come to R' Dov Zeldowitz's house.

"What can we do to honor the men of Jerusalem?" one of the town luminaries asked. "Look at the powers of the city and its citizens. They just went to pray at the Wall and G-d sent a spirit of purity to the wayward son. Two days ago he was on the lowest level, planning to spend *Seder* night at a non-kosher hotel, drinking *tereifah* wine and eating their filthy meat. And yet as the *chametz* was burned, all of Minsk knew that the lost son had been found!"

His words made a strong impression. All those present vowed to increase their donations to the Minsk Kollel in Jerusalem. Among the philanthropists was Eli Baruch himself, who donated a hefty sum from his inheritance. When the collection was finished it was found that a vast amount, 4,000 rubles, or 10,000 francs, had been pledged.

With the money a large plot of land was purchased, and the neighborhood Beit Minsk, which still stands in Jerusalem, was built.

Forming a Government

Dawn came to Lutzk.

R'LIPA STOOD BY THE WINDOWSILL LOST IN THOUGHT, hardly noticing the beauty of the sunrise. One by one the stars disappeared, leaving their nightly vigil, replaced by the emerging light. In the east, the darkness had already lifted; the approaching daybreak had painted a deep blue stripe across the sky.

He leaned heavily on his elbows, trying to support his body that was weary from a sleepless night. Oh, the body — the body was here, but the mind was far away.

R' Lipa's face grew melancholy as his thoughts wandered to a time several years earlier.

Summer 5681 (1921)

In the home of the rebbe, R' Yisrael Perlow of Stolin, confusion reigned. The rebbe's serious illness had come upon him suddenly, remorselessly devastating his tormented body. Word of the sickness had stunned his *chassidim* and followers. The rebbe was still a young man, and now he was critically ill. Several well-known doctors were immediately brought in. Their recommendations were unequivocal: Here they could do nothing; perhaps in Germany, in the large medical centers of Frankfurt-am-Main, something could be done.

The rebbe prepared for the journey, a very long journey indeed. He gave a slight hint, and the rebbetzin, understanding immediately, broke out in bitter tears. Suddenly the youngest of their six sons, R' Yochanan, walked by. His father pointed to him. "Why the crying? If all we had merited was to bring forth such a great soul into the world, *dayenu*, it would have been sufficient!"

R' Yisrael traveled to Frankfurt, but there, too, doctors couldn't find a cure, and on the second day of Rosh Hashanah 5682 (1922) his soul ascended to heaven. After a short time, three of his sons took on the leadership of various communities: In Stolin it was R' Moishele, who also opened a yeshivah in the city; R' Avraham Elimelech led the people of Karlin; and the youngest of the sons, R' Yochanan, traveled to head the community of Lutzk.

"And do the people really understand the greatness of their rebbe?" R' Lipa continued to follow the thread of his thoughts. "Does anyone know of the entire nights spent diligently learning, bent over a Gemara until dawn, like this night for example? And what does the public know of his other behaviors, when all is kept a mysterious secret and he conceals himself within his rooms?"

R' Lipa Margulies, the rebbe's *gabbai*, stood deep in meditation for a long while. Suddenly he jumped: The rebbe was standing in the doorway, looking at his faithful attendant with a gaze full of love, a gaze that held concern in it as well.

"R' Lipa, I have a request. Please ask your son, the lawyer, to come to me at 6 p.m."

The *gabbai* looked upset. The mention of his son's name did not particularly gladden him. His son had left the path of *Chassidus*, donned a short jacket, and was now a licensed attorney. The father's sole comfort was that his son had, at least, not left the path of Judaism completely.

"Father, what are you doing here?" Attorney Margulies asked, surprised by the unexpected visitor walking into his office that morning. It had been several years since he opened his practice as a lawyer, and his father had never visited his office. In fact, the opposite was true: The *gabbai* took scrupulous care to avoid the place.

"Do you have a case against someone?" he joked. "Perhaps you want to open a file?"

R' Lipa was not amused. He immediately told his son what had brought him there.

"The rebbe is asking for me?" the young attorney asked, shocked. His eyes lit up, thinking of the honor. Then they darkened again, remembering that he had left his chassidic life. Doubtless the rebbe wanted to lecture him for having turned away.

"Look, Father," he said as he tried to talk his way out of it, "tonight is really — I'm stuck in the office until very late, I've got this huge pile of paperwork. I have a tricky case tomorrow morning and I've got to be prepared before I appear in court."

"No excuses, please," his father thundered. "When the rebbe calls — you come! And not only that: You will be much better off in court tomorrow if you've gotten the rebbe's blessing tonight."

The grandfather clock chimed six rings as R' Lipa knocked on the rebbe's door that evening. His son, the attorney, stood nervously next to him, inwardly blessing the dim lighting that hid his rapidly reddening face. His confusion grew even greater when his father brought him to the rebbe and said, "*Nu*, the rebbe will do whatever is necessary."

"I know what is necessary," the rebbe answered, signaling to R' Lipa to leave them alone.

Completely at a loss, R' Lipa sat on the other side of the door, waiting for a long, long time. First he guessed that the rebbe wanted to make his son repent. Why else would he want to be alone with him? Later he decided that the rebbe must simply want to get help for some Jew who had found himself in a legal tangle.

The hands of the clock pointed to 2 in the morning. Occasionally, the muffled sound of voices emerged from the room. Infrequently R' Lipa could make out a clear word or two. He could have sworn that the rebbe once said, "Write it," and that his son once or twice said the word "Vatzelbeski," but more than that he could not discern. Finally, he fell into the sleep that was weighing down so heavily upon him.

And in the room —

"Sit down," the rebbe told the attorney. "Your father is racking his brains trying to guess why I've called you here. As you know, after several years of political chaos our nation, Poland, has decided to create a coalition government, a democracy. But the old rule, 'Whoever torments Israel becomes the head,' applies here. Most of the parties running for the Sejm, the parliament, are anti-Semitic. Their representatives are competing with each other for anti-Jewish slogans, and they're making all sorts of terrible promises to the hostile Polish public, telling them how they will persecute the Jews when they're elected.

"And now," the rebbe concluded, "I want you to tell me the names of all the candidates from all the parties and for all the positions. Begin with the prime minister and end with the other ministers. Who is running for prime minister?"

The lawyer gave a short inward prayer of thanksgiving that he had always been so interested in politics, which gave him a lot of inside knowledge of the process.

"There are two of them," he said, giving their names.

"And which one is better for the Jews?" the rebbe asked. The attorney named one of the candidates.

"How do you know?" the rebbe wouldn't let up. "Bring me proof."

Only after the attorney cited actual quotations from both candidates' speeches, proving one less anti-Semitic than the other, was the rebbe satisfied. "Open your briefcase," the rebbe suddenly commanded. The puzzled lawyer obeyed wordlessly, pulling out a pad of paper that he normally used for writing contracts, wills, and other official documents.

"And now write on it, 'So-and-So, Prime Minister.'

"And for Interior Minister, who is running?" the rebbe asked once again. He heard the names of the candidates, heard which was best for the Jews, heard the evidence.

Attorney Margulies dipped his golden fountain pen into the inkwell and, on the second line, following the rebbe's directions, wrote, "So-and-So, Interior Minister."

"And who is running for Finance Minister?"

Only at 4 in the morning did the rebbe finishing "putting together" his coalition government: 10 hours of intense deliberations brought a government that would be the very best the Jews could hope for.

When the list of ministers was complete, the rebbe said, "The list isn't worth the paper it's written on unless it has been properly notarized." The lawyer placed his notary's seal, used only on rare legal occasions, onto the paper.

Poor R' Lipa; he felt his small stock of patience running out completely. Ten hours staring at the outside of a locked door was enough to fire the imagination with all sorts of possibilities.

The door opened. He raced to his son's side.

"Listen, Father," the lawyer said, after they had walked out of the house, "your rebbe, I don't know if he's an angel or — He just put together a coalition government, with every member the candidate who has the least possibility of being elected!"

Two weeks passed. The elections were held and the results astonished all the citizenry, both Jewish and non-Jewish. Poland was abuzz. Whoever had heard such a thing: an entire government made up of the candidates who had a minute chance of election! Only a few realized that these ministers were the ones who were the best for the Jews, something that was proved again and again through the years, until the entire country fell into the hands of the Nazis with the outbreak of the Second World War.

Attorney Margulies sat in his office, the Polish newspaper open before him. Tears fell from his eyes, dropping on the paper, as he murmured, "So he is an angel. An angel."

A Covenant of Peace

A BLINDING FLASH OF WHITE LIGHTNING LIT UP THE STREET; immediately afterwards came the rolling sound of a thunderclap that shook the walls of the houses and the hearts of their inhabitants alike. A drenching rain came pouring down, cleansing everything it touched.

From the stairwell came the sound of heavy footsteps and the clatter of a piece of heavy furniture being dragged around. Occasionally the object would get stuck on a step or bang into a wall, and suddenly there would be the unexpected but not unpleasant sound of a silver bell.

"What are they moving there?" the building's residents wondered.

R' Yechiel Grossman got an immediate answer to the query. The heavy footsteps made their way directly to his door. The doorbell rang, shrill and loud compared to the silvery tones of the bells outside.

In the doorway stood an older man bathed in sweat despite the cold, his hand resting on a huge object completely covered in thick cloth. He pulled a damp piece of paper out of his pocket and tried to read it.

"Sir, perhaps you can help me. I'm looking for an address." He peered at the wet paper but finally gave up and handed it to the apartment's owner.

Yechiel glanced at the paper. The letters had been partially smudged by the wetness; decoding the handwriting would take a bit of effort. When he succeeded in deciphering the address, he looked at the porter with pity.

"It says Rabban Shimon ben Gamliel Street 17."

"But isn't this Rabban Shimon ben Gamliel?" the porter asked.

"This is Shimon Gamliel 17," Yechiel gave the aging deliveryman another regretful look. "It was a natural mistake. The address you're looking for is far from here. Even empty-handed it's a matter of about half an hour's walk, and carrying something so heavy will make it even longer."

The man raised his hands in despair. "One minute," Yechiel grabbed his hands. "I'll order a taxi."

"Absolutely not," the porter shuddered. "It would be a desecration!"

He saw Yechiel's questioning look and without a word pulled away the black nylon covering. Beneath the cloth lay a huge chair, breathtaking in its beauty, carved by an expert craftsman's hand in fine oak. Delicate carvings graced the corners, and each of the arms bore skillfully crafted clusters of grapes. Small silver bells tinkled from the back of the chair. A plaque was affixed to the backrest: "This is the chair of Eliyahu *HaNavi*, may he be remembered for good, donated for the merit of the public for the soul of the pure man, Meir Shimon Ben-Shalom."

"I knew him," the elderly porter's voice broke the silence. "He was a good man, and it is a great merit that in this beautiful chair children will be brought into the covenant of Avraham. Have you ever seen such a thing?" he asked, pride in his voice.

"Never," Yechiel stood transfixed before the chair. It was, indeed, lovely. "It's worth being a *sandek* just to be able to sit on it," he laughed.

"It's not a laughing matter," the porter said, his face somber. "This chair is the apple of the Ben-Shalom family's eye. It cost a fortune, and they only lend it out for very special circumcisions. This morning they called me to bring the chair to the *bris* being made by one of the brothers in a hall on Rabban Shimon ben Gamliel Street. Yechezkel Ben-Shalom, the father of the baby, and all his brothers are very wealthy. Because of the bad weather they paid me double to bring the chair there without damaging it."

"Who is the *sandek*?" Yechiel asked curiously.

"Oh, the *sandek* is the elderly kabbalist, R' Yaakov Levi. He's a true ascetic: It doesn't matter to him what chair he sits on, it could be a plain plastic one, but it's my job to see to it that this chair gets there as quickly as possible. I'm the one who always delivers it; no one else has ever had the job, and I will not agree to put it in a cab."

The words came out with force, as if to state that no argument would be accepted.

"Can I offer you help?" Yechiel asked hesitantly, a bit wary of how the stubborn porter would react. "Maybe we can carry the chair together."

Surprisingly, the porter agreed. "It's a good idea, because I'm afraid I won't be able to carry and protect it by myself in this heavy rain," he explained. Once again he wrapped the chair in its nylon cover, as a mother carefully swaddles her baby, making certain that no tiny crack remained open to the elements. The two of them went down to the deserted street. The rain had driven away all signs of life; everyone had sought shelter until the downpour ended.

They carried the heavy chair with great care, step by step. Yechiel, breathing heavily, wondered how the old man could carry the heavy burden by himself.

"It's actually easier by myself," the porter seemed to read his thoughts. "I put it on my back at the correct angle, tie it up with rope and go for a Shabbos stroll."

"Merciful Jews, please help us complete the *minyan*." They stopped, wondering where the call could be coming from. Someone needed a *minyan* this late in the morning? The *Shacharis* prayers were all done, and it was too early for *Minchah*.

In the doorway of an old building a man stood trembling, his woolen coat completely drenched and dripping. "Have pity, there's a *bris* here and we're only eight people. The two of you make ten."

Yechiel stood, baffled. "But we're on our way to a *bris* right now, and they're waiting for us."

"No, no, it's okay," the elderly porter interrupted. "There's at least an hour and a half until that *bris* begins. I always leave very early so that there shouldn't be a last-minute problem."

They entered the house. It was a small one, with poverty screaming out from every corner. "The *bris* was supposed to take place in the local *shul*, but the mother got sick and we can't take her out on such a stormy day. She absolutely refuses to miss out on her son's *bris*," the baby's father explained. It was clear from the deep creases on his *kippah* that it sat on his head only in honor of the occasion.

Yechiel glanced at the few participants. With the exception of the *mohel*, examining his instruments, it seemed that no one here was Torah observant.

"Who is the *sandek*?" he asked worriedly.

"The neighborhood rabbi was supposed to be *sandek*," the father muttered. "But I didn't manage to tell him that we've changed the location. He's probably waiting in the *shul*, and I don't know what to do."

Yechiel glanced at his watch. Time was passing. It would take time for someone to go call the rabbi in the *shul*, which was not nearby, and who knew if the rabbi would even be able to come in this pouring rain? And they still had to get to another *bris*, the rich man's *bris*.

"Maybe you would be *sandek*?" the father whispered to Yechiel as he stared at his glowing countenance. One look at Yechiel's face was enough to show that he was of rabbinic blood.

For lack of another solution, Yechiel agreed. "If someone would have told me half an hour ago that I'd be *sandek* at a *bris* I would have laughed, but now look —" the thought crossed his mind.

The *mohel* handed him a *tallis* and showed him an upholstered chair in the salon, a chair that had seen better days. He had almost sat down when the porter gave a shout. "Don't sit on it!"

Yechiel, startled, stared, but the porter, with a laugh, unveiled the large chair. "It seems that Heaven sent us here, to offer up a proper chair for Eliyahu *HaNavi*."

On that day Yechiel merited to do many mitzvos. After serving as *sandek*, the baby's father honored him with the blessings.

"And let his name in Yisrael be called," Yechiel stopped, hoping the name wouldn't be too cut off from the baby's Jewish heritage. Erez, perhaps, or Gai, or Yaniv, or Tomer —

"Meir Shimon," the father whispered.

"Meir Shimon?"

"Meir Shimon," the man repeated firmly.

A memory flashed through his mind, disappearing in the excitement that reigns after a *bris*, between the heartfelt congratulations and the generous cups of wine.

And the two went on their way, pulling their heavy load through the rainy streets until they arrived, dripping with raindrops and sweat alike, at the luxurious hall on Rabban Shimon ben Gamliel Street.

The difference between the two affairs was striking in its sharpness: Here all was elegance, there all was poverty. Here was wealth, there was want.

But there were two similarities between *bris* and *bris*. Like a rare gem set in a diamond-studded golden chain, the beautiful chair stood out among the luxurious appointments of the hall. And how much more did it glow in the background of the wretched apartment: There, it looked like a king's crown that had somehow fallen upon a garbage heap.

When the kabbalist R' Yaakov Levi was honored with the blessings, he stopped for a moment after the words "and let his name be called in Yisrael."

"Meir Shimon," the father whispered.

"Meir Shimon ben Yechezkel, this is the little one, he shall be big," the kabbalist continued in a confident voice, while the ladies wiped tears from the corners of their eyes.

Yechiel didn't wait until the end of the *bris*. The memory that had flashed through his mind came back again, this time causing a great stir in his consciousness. He walked behind the chair and stared at the name of the dead man in whose honor the chair had been given, the name inscribed in golden letters on a small plaque: "Meir Shimon."

Ignoring the wondering looks of the other guests Yechiel raced out of the milling hall as fast as his legs would take him. Raindrops poured down upon his head; but he ignored them. Beneath every awning and shelter pedestrians stood, trying vainly to stay dry in the downpour. Only Yechiel continued, oblivious to his dripping clothing.

When he reached the poor apartment he knocked loudly on the door and apologized for the abruptness of his interruption. In the middle of the room lay the newborn, sleeping in an old carriage.

"Tell me the truth, what is your connection with the Ben-Shalom family?" He didn't ask, he demanded an answer.

The man and his wife stared at each other, their faces growing scarlet and pale by turns. A mute argument took place between the two. Finally, the husband nodded his head in assent and the woman said simply, "I am their sister."

"Your father was —"

"He was the wealthy, well-known man, R' Meir Shimon Ben-Shalom."

Yechiel stood, mute. Sometimes a person walks blindly through thick darkness, and suddenly a flash of lightning illuminates everything. In the same way the light of understanding suddenly brightened the landscape of his mind; the mystery was solved.

And there are no coincidences in this world. Not when Rabban Shimon ben Gamliel is confused with Shimon Gamliel. Not when the name "Meir Shimon" comes up three times in one day.

And not with two *brissos* — which seemed not to have any connection with each other — that took place on the same day.

"Come with me," he grasped the husband's arm firmly and pulled him away. "We're going to a *seudas mitzvah* of your in-laws."

The man gave a backward glance at his wife, hoping the new mother would rescue him from this Jew, who was giving off waves of concern and love. But she merely nodded her head weakly, as if in agreement with Yechiel's strange behavior.

A confused silence fell upon the large hall when the two men entered. The Ben-Shalom brothers stared, paralyzed, at their estranged brother-in-law.

Yechiel ignored them. He grasped the man's hand and led him to the head table.

"Do you know this man?" he said, his voice a challenge.

An older man with a dignified demeanor stood up. "I am Binyamin Ben-Shalom, the oldest of the brothers, and it was I who, with the agreement of my family, disowned my sister and her husband, who stands before us, until they would agree to leave their wayward path and return to the Jewish traditions."

Yechiel approached the old porter who was mingling with the crowd and whispered something to him. The two of them then went together to the venerable kabbalist, R' Yaakov Levi. The brother-in-law, too, spoke with the kabbalist for some moments, frequently nodding his head.

The heavy silence that had fallen upon the hall during this time was broken by the elderly mystic.

"Gentlemen," he announced loudly. The participants turned their eyes to him, trying not to miss a single word. "We have seen wondrous things today. The respected brothers of the Ben-Shalom family disowned their sister and her husband, because they had left the true path, and this was to remain in effect until they returned. Now I have been told all that took place with the chair of Eliyahu, and this astonishing event, and therefore I say that there is no doubt that a spark of *teshuvah* has flared in the sister and her husband. And that is why the Creator saw to it that the chair, named for her father, should reach her home so that they could make use of it. Everything is the will of the Creator. And the husband has attested to their wish to return and take on the yoke of Heaven.

"Therefore I decree," R' Yaakov turned to the startled brothers, "that since your vow was conditional, it is clear that your sister has done *teshuvah*. Your vow is annulled, doesn't exist, and from now on your sister shall return to her father's inheritance."

Not Worth a Bullet

THE STREETS OF UMAN WORE A CLOAK OF DARKNESS. The Russian cold penetrated deep into the bones, and the wailing wind made it that much worse. The moon, full on this midmonth night, couldn't find a single crack in the monolithic wall of deep, dark clouds that covered the sky over Uman, from one end to the other.

On nights such as these, people seek shelter in their heated homes, and cuddle beneath down blankets for a sweet night's sleep.

Such frosty nights are a blessing to the Soviet secret police, the notorious NKVD, whose very name casts terror in the hearts of the country's citizenry. Who would be foolish enough to go out in such weather? Even the worst of criminals wouldn't dare leave the warm walls of their homes.

A few shadowy figures approached one such home in the Jewish neighborhood. They staked out the building, and ultimately surrounded it.

In this house lived one of the most dangerous of men, a Jew whose very existence undermined the foundations of the state. The dangerous felon was a black-bearded man of about 40, possessor of a pair of eyes that burned like hot coals, a man whose inner core burned with the fear of heaven, whose entire body was aflame with fervor.

This was R' Levi Yitzchak Bender, one of the pillars of the Breslover *chassidim* in Uman, later to gain fame as one of Jerusalem's wondrous inhabitants, both among Yerushalmis and particularly among the Breslover *chassidim*. Many would later be pulled into his orbit, great men who sought to learn from him one particular, and difficult, topic: service of G-d.

That mighty country, the evil state of Josef Stalin, was more afraid of its Jews than anything else. Its atheistic government felt deeply threatened by the Jewish spirit. This holy spirit frightened the Soviet leadership much more than the real counterrevolution-ary movements, that were also put down with an iron fist.

The house was dark, not surprising in view of the lateness of the hour. But the darkness did not put the silent policemen's fears to rest; they approached the house with their pistols ready to fire. They walked over to a window and knocked on it harshly.

"Does Bender live here?" the shout disturbed the peace of the night.

"Yes, yes," R' Levi Yitzchak answered innocently. He knew that he was on the government's "hit list," but had not realized that he would be taken so soon.

The door was pulled roughly off its hinges, making a terrible noise. The men jumped inside like hunting dogs bearing down on their prey. A minute passed and R' Levi Yitzchak was pulled out of the house, and taken to the prison in Uman.

A deep feeling of mourning descended upon the family. R' Levi Yitzchak's wife and daughter (today Mrs. Ettel Lasker of Bnei Brak) wandered outside the prison, waiting for the moment when they would be allowed to enter. A terrible sense of anxiety grew within them: Everyone knew that often people taken to the cellars of the NKVD never returned. Years of exile in Siberia was not the harshest punishment meted out in those times; people accused of crimes, many of them not particularly serious, sometimes disappeared for-ever within the torture chambers of the NKVD, their bodies never recovered.

R' Levi Yitzchak didn't have to ask what he was being accused of. He had helped many Jews financially, allowing them to survive both physically and spiritually. The Jewish section of the govern-ment, the cursed Yevsektzia, had been following his tracks careful-ly, and his underground activities had been marked as very serious. The noose had been tightening around his neck these many months. Innocent-looking bystanders had been standing around and watching his every move, and wandering near his house, care-fully noting who entered and who exited. Everything was written down. Spies dressed as Jews took part in the Shabbos get-togethers of the *chassidim* in the *beis midrash*, washing their hands for the Shabbos meals together with the others. R' Levi Yitzchak said his *divrei* Torah; every word was written down and filed.

R' Levi Yitzchak knew that he was endangering himself, but he could not stop. He had saved many Torah-observant Jews from absolute starvation. His messengers had traveled as far as Poland seeking contributions for the huge charity organization that he founded together with his friend, R' Eliyahu Chaim Ruzhin. This fund supported Uman's Torah students and those who still bore the torch of Judaism.

He was, indeed, maintaining a religious organization — an unspeakable crime.

R' Levi Yitzchak knew the gravity of his situation and understood clearly what he would be accused of. But the long years of spiritual exercises, of adapting himself to all circumstances, culled from the teachings of R' Nachman of Breslov, now proved themselves. A true and faithful *chassid* never panics. The mind rules the heart! His knees did not buckle as he walked through the corridors of the Uman prison. R' Levi Yitzchak entered the prison standing straight and tall, like a captured prince.

He stood in one corner, a lone Jew among dozens of gentiles. There he was left, forgotten, in a foul room, together with the dregs of humanity who tormented him with their filthy language. As he told later, from the beginning of the ordeal, in those first minutes, he recited to himself the first 13 essays of *Likutei Moharan*, R' Nachman's great work.

R' Eliyahu Chaim Ruzhin, R' Levi Yitzchak's friend, had also been arrested. Both men were charged with more than just an ordinary criminal infraction. The government sought much more.

"You are accused of political crimes, of counterrevolutionary activity. You are fighting the revolution," the investigator read from a thick file, his face stern.

The punishment for such a crime ranged from three years, in the event of a slight infraction, and up to the hangman's noose if the crime was a serious one.

R' Levi Yitzchak did not know which end of the spectrum his activities fell upon. But he knew one thing: Twenty-seven *chassidim* from the same group in Uman, all good friends, had been sent into exile, and all traces of them had been lost. What difference was there between him and them?

The interrogations began. They were interrogations whose sole purpose was to break the man's spirit and turn him into an empty husk. Every day he was brought for questioning, each day more brutal than the day before. After each interrogation, he was given a sheaf of papers to sign. But his hand never closed upon the pen: He knew they did not want to punish only him, and one signature would bring in its wake the imprisonment of an entire group of Jews whose only crime was the desire to keep the mitzvos.

R' Levi Yitzchak would not break. His interrogators startled him when they revealed their detailed knowledge of every facet of his life. His heart missed a beat or two when they told over the *divrei Torah* he said in *shul*, word for word! But he did not surrender. His immensely powerful spirit was steel forged, and he faced the hellish interrogations with unparalleled strength of character.

And there were moments of contentment, too, when his family came to visit him. "Father," his daughter, Ettel, said emotionally, "you've done so much good in your life, G-d will surely not desert you."

It was a drop of comfort in the black sea surrounding him. He continued to fight obstinately against his interrogators.

But the interrogators would not relent either.

R' Levi Yitzchak sat across from his interrogator, his heart thumping. His various tormentors had been tearing him into shreds; still, he kept his lips sealed. Occasionally he would argue with the officer seated across the desk from him, vehemently asserting that all the charges were pure lies.

The door suddenly crashed open. The commander of the prison himself stepped into the room. He had come to witness the interrogation procedures. For a short time he sat and listened silently to the debate raging between the interrogator and his prisoner; soon, though, he lost patience.

"Enough," he yelled furiously. "Why are you arguing with this disgusting Jew, when you've got a gun in your holster! Shoot him and be done with it."

The interrogator's emotionless eyes gazed coolly at the Jew sitting before him with bowed head, then met the furious gaze of his superior officer.

"This wretched Jew," he pointed at R' Levi Yitzchak, "isn't even worth the bullet it would take to kill him. What a shame for the Supreme Soviet to waste even five kopeks on him; he'll explode on his own, without a bullet."

Four months passed, an endless nightmare in the walls of the Uman prison. The tortures darkened his features, but did not break his spirit.

After one third of a year, the investigation was completed. The file was sent to Kiev, to the NKVD officer appointed over the entire region; to the man who held the fate of 40 million men and women in his hands, whose word decided which ones would be killed and which would be spared.

The command followed soon afterwards: Bring the prisoner to Kiev.

"To Kiev? Impossible!" R' Levi Yitzchak's cellmate cast a pair of astonished eyes at him. This was the former prison supervisor, who himself had been cast down into the jail he had once ruled. "I know the procedure," he muttered. "It takes months from the time an investigation is concluded and the results are sent to Kiev, until they get an answer from there. Your investigation just ended now. No, it's impossible," the man concluded firmly.

"We have been told that tomorrow we are being transferred to the prison in Kiev," R' Levi Yitzchak answered shortly. "Those are the facts, whether or not you agree."

"Oh, I understand," the former warden said, with a dreary smile. "Don't you believe it. You'll never get to Kiev alive — you'll be assassinated on the way."

An honor guard escorted those dangerous criminals, R' Levi Yitzchak Bender and R' Eliyahu Chaim Ruzhin, on their journey to Kiev. As they marched, heavy-featured guards and secret policemen guarded them to their right and to their left. Riders on horseback, too, kept a close eye on the prisoners.

From the corner of his eye R' Levi Yitzchak could see one other prisoner being transferred to Kiev. This one had been condemned to death for murder. The security around the killer was much laxer than around the two *chassidim*.

One prayer surged through R' Levi Yitzchak: "May we only merit a Jewish burial." He no longer believed he would come out alive from this journey; he had heard too much of what awaited them in Kiev.

As if to intensify their fears, the guards placed them in the center of the road and ordered them to walk only there, adding a stern warning: If they took one step to the left or the right, even to avoid oncoming traffic, they would be shot immediately.

After this, the two were placed in a pitch-black vehicle known as "the Black Car." The name alone sent shivers down the spine of any who heard it. People who climbed into those dark automobiles were invariably never heard of again.

The conclusion was clear. The shadow of the scaffold was growing larger.

"You're members of the Breslov group?"

"Yes," R' Levi Yitzchak answered.

He was sitting across from the warden of the Kiev prison, a man who could send him to his death without lifting an eyebrow.

The two prisoners had arrived at the prison a short time earlier, and had been placed together in a room. All the signs indicated that they would be executed that very night.

R' Levi Yitzchak looked at the warden's desk, stunned. It was painted a bright red. "They're called the Red Army for a reason," the thought flitted through his mind. "He is red, his house is red, his table is red. Blood red."

The warden asked him a few questions. He seemed friendly

enough, but R' Levi Yitzchak was not a fool. He waited fearfully to hear his verdict.

Were his ears playing tricks on him? "You want to go free. Okay, you're free."

"I don't believe it," he whispered.

"Look at this Jew," the warden turned to his secretary. "So low in his own eyes, he can't believe that we're letting him go."

But the miracle did not end here. The warden asked where the two prisoners planned on going. R' Levi Yitzchak, suspecting a trap, and fearing that they would follow him to see which Jew, which counterrevolutionary, he would flee to, said he was going to sleep in the Vagzahl train station.

The warden ordered his secretary to give the men a generous sum of money so that they could rent a warm room in the area near the station. After all, it was the brutal Russian winter.

Only later did R' Levi Yitzchak learn that the warden of the Kiev prison was also a Jew, the son-in-law of a Breslover *chassid*. His father-in-law had long before warned his son-in-law, a loyal Communist, that if he ever had the opportunity to help Breslover *chassidim*, he must do so.

And ultimately he paid a heavy price: When the fact that the prisoners had been freed became known, the warden was sentenced to death.

"Remember," the aged R' Levi Yitzchak would repeat, over and over, to the *chassidim* listening to him in the *beis midrash* in Jerusalem. "Remember His miracles, and the lovingkindness of G-d. His salvation comes in the blink of an eye: Within minutes the circle of death had turned to life. Remember!"

Midnight with R' Levi Yitzchak

"On that day Hashem will be One and His Name will be One." The last echoes of *Maariv* melted into the evening's darkness; the congregants wended their way home through the labyrinthine streets.

R' Levi Yitzchak, too, strode through the narrow street that led from the *beis midrash* to his home in the adjoining neighborhood. A person's eye could cry at the sight of the average old man carrying his 90 years beneath his stooped back.

Carrying his years? Not R' Levi Yitzchak. The opposite: It seemed that 90 years of life were dancing and carrying him in its arms. His back stayed erect because of an internal support, the brightness of *Chassidus* straightened his spine, keeping him so strong that he could look Satan right in the eye: "Off with you; here you will find no place!" But it is the nature of mankind to see only the physical that stands before them, paying no attention to the noble world of the spirit that lies beneath it.

When R' Levi Yitzchak reached the stairway that led to his house he climbed up with surprising ease and agility. His escort, a young man, was amazed. "What's the hurry?"

And R' Levi Yitzchak looked wonderingly at the man who did not understand.

"Don't you know? We're hurrying to *tikkun chatzos*."

Oh, you who get up early — who rush to *shul* for sunrise prayers while the darkness still surrounds you — the old man has still beat you. No matter how early you rise, you will never be able to come before R' Levi Yitzchak. He will always be there before you, sitting at his table, immersed in his study.

From the time that R' Levi Yitzchak joined the Breslover *chassidim*, he had taken upon himself as immutable law to say *tikkun chatzos* every night, to wail and cry for the misery of the *Shechinah's* exile.

R' Levi Yitzchak joined in the sorrow of the *Shechinah* in exile, both when he lived in Uman and in Jerusalem. And in Kivalitesh, where his son-in-law lived, and in Samarkand and Tashkent, in a displaced persons camp in Ad-Reichnel and in Moscow.

Wherever R' Levi Yitzchak found himself in exile, the *Shechinah* was banished with him. He never forgot the destruction of the Temple, not during the day, and especially not during the night.

"Tikkun Chatzos" of R' Levi Yitzchak became almost legendary in the annals of Breslover *Chassidus*. The elders of the community stared with respectful awe at the venerable and stubborn old man who did not know the meaning of the word compromise, who would not give up even one night, even when he was ill and suffering. Young men tried to learn from him how to struggle with the lure of sleep night after night, how to struggle and to emerge victorious. A few of them, such as the young man who escorted him that night, merited being close to him during those hours, to witness the incredible scene. Many felt the stirrings of envy at a man who was completely free of the fetters of fatigue, who knew absolutely, even before he went to bed, that in a little while he would awaken, refreshed and invigorated, to serve his Creator.

How many men can really know that?

"But now?" the young man escorting him looked at his watch. The night was just beginning: What was the hurry? There were many hours yet to midnight!

But R' Levi Yitzchak was not hurrying. Indeed, the concept of hurry did not exist in his lexicon. Instead, he lived by concepts such as composure, contemplation, diligence, and never-ending reckoning of the world.

Yes, R' Levi Yitzchak was a very paragon of reckoning. He reckoned every hour, every minute. His calendar, his watch were his guides. In this he resembled the *Imrei Emes* of Gur. Once, when another great man apologized for being late for a journey they were to take together — "It seems that I was 'above time,'" he said jokingly — the *Imrei Emes* answered, "No! Time is the highest thing. There is nothing above it, only below!"

R' Levi Yitzchak's day was carefully considered and scheduled, down to the minute. A five-minute span was an entire world for him; a two-minute lateness by a *chavrusah*, a learning partner, an almost unforgivable act.

R' Levi Yitzchak reckoned and found that if one did not waste time and ate dinner right after *Maariv*, it was possible to "grab" a short nap, even during the summer months, before midnight. Not to mention the long winter nights.

Immediately after *Maariv*, therefore, they sat down to eat in the small kitchen. When he was *bentching*, R' Levi Yitzchak took his time over the blessing "*Rachem na*," particularly on the words "and on the great and holy house which bears Your Name."

"Why does he have to wake up for *tikkun chatzos*?" the thought flashed through the young man's mind, as he listened to his sweetly passionate request, "and build Jerusalem, the holy city." "Can someone ask more fervently than this?"

But that very night he saw his error.

The jangle of the alarm clock filled the large room with shrill echoes, pulling him cruelly out of his sleep. Confused, he sat up, fumbling for the cup and bowl like a blind man. When he finally managed to get his eyes open he saw R' Levi Yitzchak putting on his *gartel*.

In those first minutes he almost regretted his plan. The early rising was so difficult. He was like a drunken man, still lost in the fuzzy edges of a dream, a dream that seemed to beckon him back to the world of sleep.

A moment later he was stunned by the burning sensation of humiliation.

"What an embarrassment to you, a young man," he tormented himself. "R' Levi Yitzchak, a Jew who is into his 90s, already putting on his *gartel* while you, a 25-year-old, are still fumbling around for *negel vasser*."

The thought sent him jumping out of bed. He hastily took a seat on a low stool not far from R' Levi Yitzchak.

"Not far," he realized, was a relative term. In the physical sense the old man was no more than an arm's length away; in the realm of the spirit, though, great distances separated the two.

The young man felt that he had not managed to throw off the last vestiges of sleep. R' Levi Yitzchak was already awash with tears.

"L-rd, gentiles have come into Your portion, they have desecrated Your holy sanctuary..."

The street was silent, sleeping; only the quiet tears of R' Levi Yitzchak wafted through the air:

"Your beloved has gone with him to the heavens, I have sinned and he is in chains."

His eyes at that moment resembled the constellations; all of the heavenly bodies seemed to have come down onto the earth to participate in his awesome tears, in his mournful lament.

"*Shechinah*, what do you say..."

"And I thought *bentching* was enough." The young man was deeply moved by the sight. In his life he'd never seen such a thing. On this night those words, *tikkun chatzos*, had gained a new meaning. With a sudden understanding it became clear to him that such a level of empathy with the pain of the *Shechinah* was reached only after years of backbreaking toil, without compromise or concession, from an inner discipline harsh as those of a soldier in battle.

A soldier such as R' Levi Yitzchak, for example.

A maze of thoughts and feelings were the portion of the onlooker. R' Levi Yitzchak himself was completely absorbed in another world, at one with the weeping of our mother Rachel, in the "*tikkun Rachel*," negating himself completely in conjunction with the tears of our mother Leah, in "*tikkun Leah*."

"Until when will I be astonished, at two destructions?" His head facing heaven, as if asking his Creator, his eyes filled with tears. "Until when will You not have mercy on Jerusalem?" He begged like a child pleading with a father.

"R' Levi Yitzchak sometimes reaches a new height, approaches closer and closer to his Creator, while I stay behind, pulled down by the power of the physical," the young man thought. That night his feelings changed several times. Now he wondered how he had ever wanted to stay in bed at midnight.

From this old man's room one received a new perspective on life's purpose; here, priorities were completely rearranged.

When the time for *tikkun chatzos* was over, R' Levi Yitzchak turned to his books, to his prescribed lessons, learning until dawn.

The young man's throat went dry. He had given up on his morning cup of coffee, but what about a drink of water?

But R' Levi Yitzchak shuddered even at the thought of drinking something before *davening Shacharis*.

On the way to the *beis midrash*, in the pale bluish light that precedes dawn, the young man could not control himself.

"How can it be? To fast for so many hours? To get up at midnight, stay up until after sunrise prayers, without a drop of water?"

"Why not?" R' Levi Yitzchak was surprised. "This horse," he said, pointing to his body, "this donkey, whatever you get it used to in its youth, that's what stays with it all its life. It's all just a question of habit."

R' Levi Yitzchak was not ruled by his spirit; he ruled his spirit completely.

This volume is part of
THE ARTSCROLL SERIES®
an ongoing project of
translations, commentaries and expositions
on Scripture, Mishnah, Talmud, Halachah,
liturgy, history, the classic Rabbinic writings,
biographies and thought.

For a brochure of current publications
visit your local Hebrew bookseller
or contact the publisher:

Mesorah Publications, ltd
4401 Second Avenue
Brooklyn, New York 11232
(718) 921-9000